Fourier series

Mathematics for Engineers

The series is designed to provide engineering students in colleges and universities with a mathematical toolkit, each book including the mathematics in an engineering context. Numerous worked examples, and problems with answers, are included.

1. Laplace and z-transforms
2. Ordinary differential equations
3. Complex numbers
4. Fourier series
5. Differentiation and integration
6. Linear equations and matrices

Mathematics for Engineers

Fourier series

W. Bolton

Addison Wesley Longman Limited
Edinburgh Gate, Harlow,
Essex, CM20 2JE, England
and Associated Companies throughout the world.

First published 1995
Second impression 1997
Third impression 1999

British Library Cataloguing in Publication Data
A catalogue entry for this title is available from the British Library

ISBN 0-582-23934-6

Printed in Malaysia, TCP

Contents

Preface

This is one of the books in a series designed to provide engineering students in colleges and universities with a mathematical toolkit. In the United Kingdom it is aimed primarily at HNC/HND students and first-year undergraduates. Thus the mathematics assumed is that in BTEC National Certificates and Diplomas, GNVQ Advanced level or in A level. The pace of development of the mathematics has been aimed at the notional reader for whom mathematics is not their prime interest or "best subject" but need the mathematics in their other studies. The mathematics is developed and applied in an engineering context with large numbers of worked examples and problems, all with answers being supplied.

This book is concerned with the Fourier series and an introduction to the Fourier transform and their application in engineering. It does need some mathematics which might not have been covered in BTEC National or A level courses and thus might need to follow some further mathematics course, e.g. the calculus in the book *Differentiation and integration* and complex numbers in the book *Complex numbers* in this series. A familarity with basic algebra, complex numbers and calculus is assumed. In particular the text requires familarity with the handling of trigonometric identities and complex numbers, the integration of trigonometric functions and the technique of integration by parts. An Appendix giving supporting mathematics on these points is included. The aim of the book has been to include sufficient worked examples and problems to enable the reader to acquire some understanding and proficiency in the the use of Fourier series and transforms. These can then be used when dealing with periodic waveforms which are non-sinusoidal or distorted sinsusoidal, and signals which are non-repetitive.

W. Bolton

1 Periodic waveforms

1.1 Waveforms

This book is about the Fourier series. The series provides a set of mathematical tools which enables waveforms of any form to be broken down into a number of sinusoidal waves with different frequencies. In this chapter we will consider how we can mathematically describe sinusoidal and non-sinusoidal periodic waves. In chapter 2 the Fourier series is introduced.

1.1.1 Periodic and aperiodic waveforms

Consider the signal with the sinusoidal waveform shown in figure 1.1(a). The graph shows how the value of the signal varies with time. The values of the signal keep on repeating themselves every T seconds. Figure 1.1(b) shows a signal with a triangular waveform. Figure 1.1(c) shows a pulsed waveform. Their values keep on repeating themselves every T seconds. Such waveforms are called periodic. A *periodic waveform* is defined as being one for which the entire set of values repeats itself at regular intervals; the time between successive repetitions being called the *periodic time* or *period* (T).

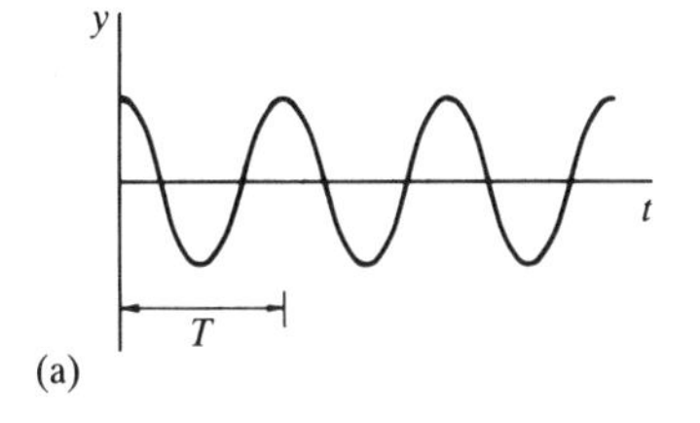

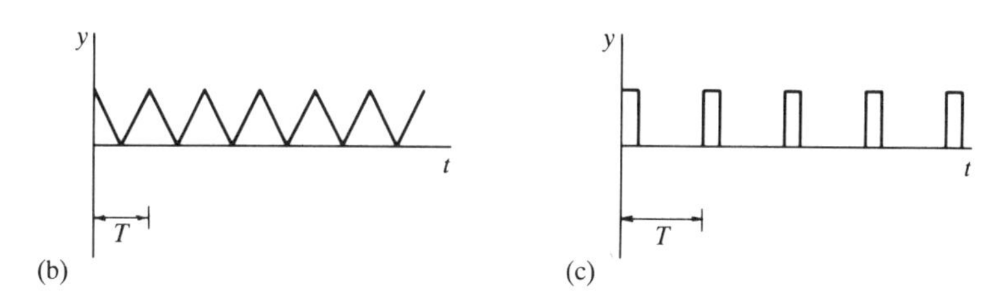

Fig. 1.1 Examples of periodic waveforms

In mathematical terms, we can define a function of time $f(t)$ as being periodic if the function has the same value when considered at a time $t + T$, i.e.

$$f(t) = f(t + T) \quad [1]$$

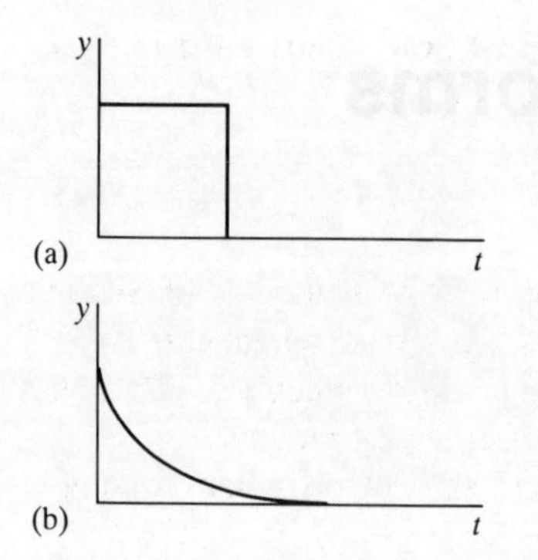

Fig. 1.2 Examples of aperiodic waveforms

for all values of time t. T is the periodic time. Thus if a waveform has a periodic time of 3 s then we must have $f(t) = f(t + 3)$.

Figure 1.2(a) shows a signal which consists of just a single pulse. This signal does not have values which keep on repeating themselves. Figure 1.2(b) shows a signal which just decays away with time. This signal also has values which do not repeat themselves. The term *aperiodic* is used for signals which do not repeat themselves.

1.2 The sinusoidal waveform

Figure 1.3 shows how we can generate a sinusoidal waveform. The oscillating value y is a function of time (we really should write it as $y(t)$ to indicate this) and is the vertical projection of a rotating radius arm of length A. y is mathematically described by

$$y = A \sin \theta \qquad [2]$$

where θ is the angle the radius arm makes the horizontal axis.

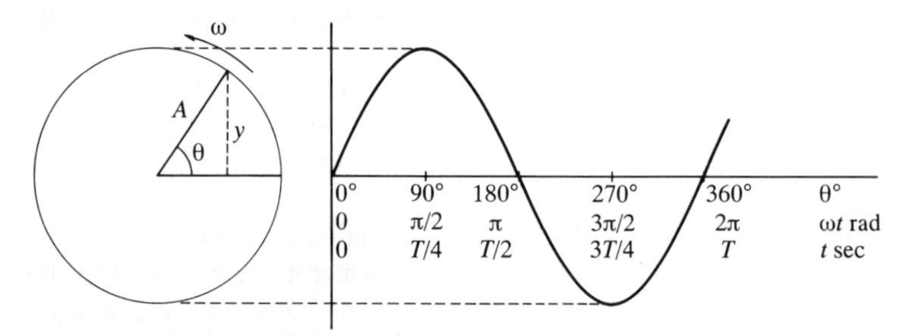

Fig. 1.3 Generating $y = A \sin \theta$

When $\theta = 0°$ then $y = 0$. As θ increases from 0° to 90° so the value of y increases from 0 to A. As θ increases from 90° to 180° so the value of y decreases from A to 0. From 180° to 270° the value of y changes from 0 to $-A$ and from 270° to 360° from $-A$ to 0. From 360° onwards the set of values repeats itself, this repetition occurring every 360°. A 360° rotation thus corresponds to the periodic time T. The value of y thus oscillates between 0 and $\pm A$, with A being termed the *amplitude*.

If the radius arm rotates with a constant angular velocity ω then the angle θ rotated in a time t is given by

$$\theta = \omega t \qquad [3]$$

The unit of angular velocity is radians/second with 2π radians being equal to one complete rotation of 360°. Thus equation [2] can be written as

$$y = A \sin \omega t \qquad [4]$$

The radius arm starts in the horizontal position at time $t = 0$. When $\omega t = 0$ then $y = 0$, when $\omega t = \pi/2$ rad then $y = A$, when $\omega t = \pi$ rad then $y = 0$, when $\omega t = 3\pi/2$ rad then $y = -A$, when $\omega t = 2\pi$ rad then $y = 0$. The waveform repeats itself every 2π radians.

The time taken to complete one revolution when rotating with an angular velocity ω is $2\pi/\omega$. Thus the periodic time T is

$$T = \frac{2\pi}{\omega} \qquad [5]$$

The *frequency* of the waveform is the number of complete waves or cycles completed per second. Thus, since it takes the periodic time T to complete one cycle, the frequency is $1/T$. Hence $f = \omega/2\pi$ or

$$\omega = 2\pi f \qquad [6]$$

The angular velocity is thus the frequency multiplied by 2π. For this reason it is often referred to as the *angular frequency*. Thus equation [4] can be written as

$$y = A \sin 2\pi f t$$

If we had started with the radius arm in the vertical position at time $t = 0$, i.e. measured θ from the vertical axis, then the equation would be

$$y = A \cos \theta = A \cos \omega t \qquad [7]$$

Figure 1.4 shows the resulting graph.

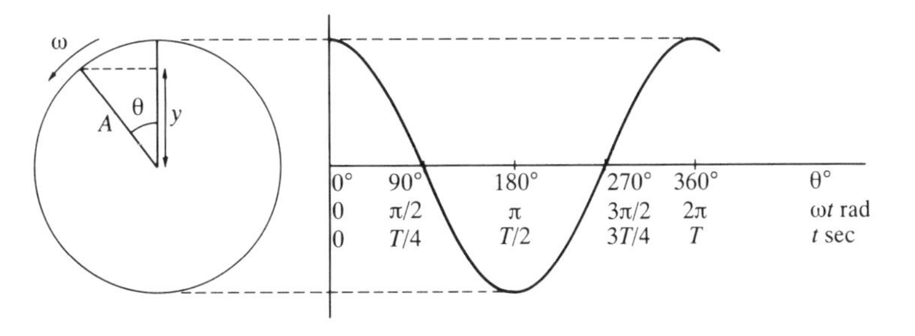

Fig. 1.4 Generating $y = A \cos \theta$

Example

What are the values of the waveform given by $y = 2 \sin \omega t$ when (a) $\omega t = \pi/4$ rad, (b) $\omega t = 0.2$ rad, (c) $\omega t = 5\pi/4$?

(a) We can use a calculator which enables us to directly determine the value of sines when the angle is in radians. Alternatively, since 2π radians correspond to 360° then $\pi/4$ radians correspond to

$$\frac{\pi}{4} \times \frac{360°}{2\pi} = 45°$$

Thus $y = 2 \sin 45° = 1.41$.
(b) 0.2 rad corresponds to

$$0.2 \times \frac{360°}{2\pi} = 11.5°$$

Thus $y = 2 \sin 11.5° = 0.40$.
(c) $5\pi/4$ rad corresponds to

$$\frac{5\pi}{4} \times \frac{360°}{2\pi} = 225°$$

Thus $y = 2 \sin 225° = -1.41$.

Example

Determine the values of y for a waveform given by $y = 3 \sin 2t$ for times t of (a) 0.1 s, (b) 0.5 s, (c) 1 s.
(a) With a time of 0.1 s we have $y = 3 \sin 0.2$. We can use a calculator which enables us directly to obtain this sine of an angle in radians, alternatively, since 2π radians correspond to 360° then 0.2 rad is $0.2 \times (360°/2\pi) = 11.5°$. Hence $y = 0.60$.
(b) For $t = 0.5$ s we have $y = 3 \sin 1.0 = 2.52$.
(c) For $t = 1$ s we have $y = 3 \sin 2 = 2.73$.

Review problems

1 Sketch the graphs, for one cycle, corresponding to the equations (a) $y = 2 \sin \theta$, (b) $y = 3 \cos \theta$.
2 What are the values of the waveform given by $y = 3 \cos \omega t$ when (a) $\omega t = 0$, (b) $\omega t = \pi/3$, (c) $\omega t = \pi/2$, (d) $\omega t = 5\pi/3$?
3 What are the values of the waveform given by $y = 2 \sin 10t$ when (a) $t = 0.1$ s, (b) $t = 0.2$ s, (c) $t = 0.3$ s, (d) $t = 0.5$ s?

1.2.1 Phase angle

In the preceding section the sine waveform generated by a rotating

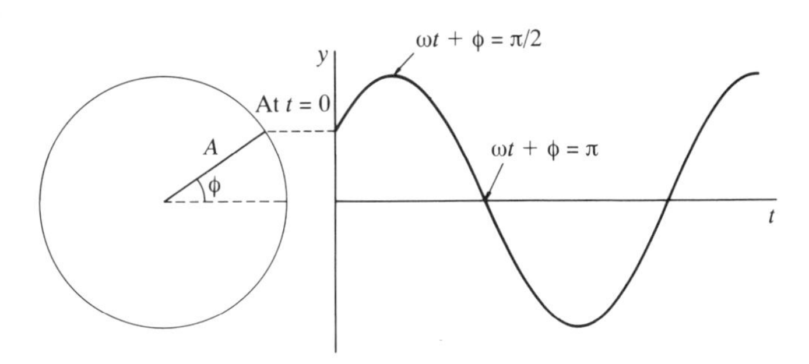

Fig. 1.5 Generating $y = A \sin (wt + \phi)$

radius arm was considered for waves that started at the time $t = 0$ with the value a zero angle and hence a value for y of 0. Consider what happens if we start the radius arm at an angle ϕ at time $t = 0$. Figure 1.5 shows the situation. The waveform is described by the equation

$$y = A \sin(\omega t + \phi) \qquad [8]$$

The angle ϕ is referred to as the *phase angle*.

The radius arm starts with an angle of ϕ relative to the horizontal position at time $t = 0$. When

$\omega t = 0$ then $y = A \sin \phi$
$\omega t = \pi/2$ rad then $y = A \sin (\pi/2 + \phi)$

We have

$y = 0$ when $\omega t + \phi = 0$ or π or 2π rad
$y = A$ when $\omega t = \pi/2$ rad
$y = -A$ when $\omega t + \phi = 3\pi/2$ rad

The waveform repeats itself every 2π radians.

Note that often the phase angle is given in degrees rather than radians. In this text, where degrees are involved, the degree symbol is always used. Thus we might have, for example,

$$y = 10 \sin (100t + 45^\circ)$$

Such an equation has, in the bracketed term, a mixture of units: the $100t$ being in radians and the 45 in degrees. If both the terms were expressed in radians then, since $45^\circ = \pi/4$ rad,

$$y = 10 \sin (100t + \pi/4)$$

In evaluating such expressions at a specific instant of time, e.g. a time of $t = 0.1$ s, then everything in the brackets needs to be in the same units before they can be added. Thus we might convert the

$100t$ to degrees so it can be added to the 45° or convert 45° to radians so it can be added to $100t$.

We can consider the waveform given by $y = A \cos \omega t$, i.e. figure 1.4, as merely being the sine waveform displaced by 90°, i.e. $y = A \sin(\omega t + \pi/2)$. Thus the term *sinusoidal waveform* is used to describe the waveforms generated by both the sine and cosine functions.

Example

Determine the values of y for the waveform given by the equation $y = 2 \sin(3t + \pi/3)$ when (a) $t = 0$, (b) $t = 0.1$ s, (c) $t = 0.2$ s.

(a) With $t = 0$ we have $y = 2 \sin \pi/3 = 1.73$.
(b) With $t = 0.1$ s we have $y = 2 \sin(0.3 + \pi/3) = 1.95$.
(c) With $t = 0.2$ s we have $y = 2 \sin(0.6 + \pi/3) = 1.99$.

Review problems

4 Determine the values of y for the waveform given by the equation $y = 2 \sin(10t + \pi/4)$ when (a) $t = 0$, (b) $t = 0.1$ s, (c) $t = 0.2$ s.

1.2.2 Harmonics

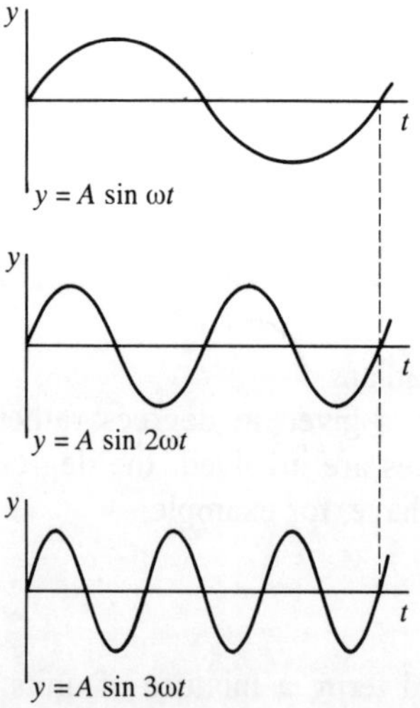

Consider graphs of the waveforms given by the equations

$$y = A \sin \omega t$$

$$y = A \sin 2\omega t$$

$$y = A \sin 3\omega t$$

where ω is a common value of angular frequency, i.e. a common angular velocity for the radius arm used to generate the three waveforms. Figure 1.6 shows the graphs. The waveform given by $A \sin \omega t$ is called the *fundamental* or *first harmonic*. It describes a waveform which has one cycle completed in one rotation of the radius arm. The waveform given by $A \sin 2\omega t$ is called the *second harmonic*. It describes a waveform which has two cycles completed in one rotation of the radius arm. This is because the angles given by the rotating radius arm are all doubled. The waveform given by $A \sin 3\omega t$ is called the *third harmonic* and has three cycles completed in one rotation of the radius arm. This is because the angles given by the rotating radius arm are all trebled.

In general, harmonics are described by an equation of the form

$$y = A \sin(n\omega t + \phi) \qquad [9]$$

y
t
$y = A \sin \omega t$
y
t
$y = A \sin 2\omega t$
y
t
$y = A \sin 3\omega t$

Fig. 1.6 First, second and third harmonics

where n is an integer with the value 1 for the first harmonic, 2 for the second harmonic, 3 for the third harmonic, etc.

Example

What will be the equation and frequency of the third harmonic if the fundamental is given by $y = 10 \sin 20t$?

The harmonics are given by $y = A \sin n\omega t$, where ω is the angular frequency of the fundamental. Thus for the third harmonic we have

$$y = 10 \sin (3 \times 20t) = 10 \sin 60t$$

The third harmonic will have an angular frequency of 60 rad/s and hence a frequency of $60/2\pi = 9.5$ Hz.

Review problems

5 What will be the equation and frequency of the fourth harmonic if the fundamental is given by $y = 10 \sin 100t$?
6 If the fundamental has a frequency of 100 Hz, what will be the frequency of the fifth harmonic?

1.3 Non-sinusoidal periodic waveforms

Periodic waveforms are not always sinusoidal. Figure 1.7 shows some examples of non-sinusoidal periodic waveforms. In each case, the periodic time is the shortest time interval before repetition occurs.

We can describe such waveforms in mathematical terms by writing equations to describe the form within a period. The equations can then describe the form over any following period since the waveform has the same form over each period. Consider, for example, the waveform in figure 1.7(a). Between the times of

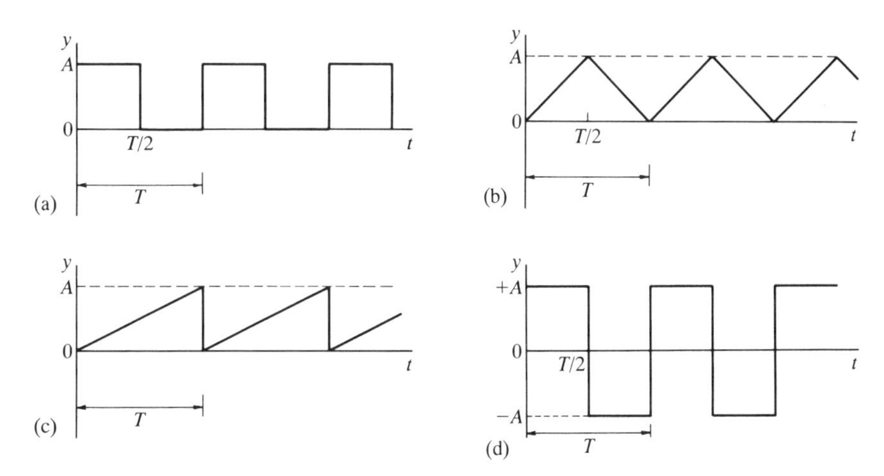

Fig. 1.7 Examples of non-sinusoidal periodic waveforms

$t = 0$ and $t = T/2$ the waveform is described by the equation $y = A$. Between $t = T/2$ and $t = T$ the waveform is described by $y = 0$. The waveform is thus generally described as

$$y = A \text{ for } 0 \le t < T/2$$
$$y = 0 \text{ for } T/2 \le t < T, \text{ period } T$$

Note that there is no description of the vertical lines at $T/2$ and T, these being merely assumed as required to link the lines described by the above equations in order to give continuity. The description in fact describes continuous bits of waveform which at their ends, i.e. $T/2$ and T, exhibit a discontinuity and jump to the next bit of waveform, the vertical lines merely being added on the assumption that the waveform is continuous without any breaks.

A function whose graph has no breaks is termed a *continuous function*. The above waveform can be termed as *piecewise continuous* in that it consists of continuous pieces with a finite number of discontinuities in any given interval of time.

Example

Describe the waveform shown in figure 1.7(b) by mathematical expressions.

For the waveform in figure 1.7(b) we have a ramp which starts with the value 0 at $t = 0$ and increases to A at the time $t = T/2$. The slope of this ramp signal is thus $A/(T/2)$ and so the value at a time t is $t \times A/(T/2)$. After time $T/2$ there is a ramp signal which drops from a value of A to 0 at time $t = T$. The slope of this ramp signal is thus $-A/(T/2)$. If we extended this ramp line back to $t = 0$ then it would cut the axis at $y = 2A$. Thus, since the standard form of the equation for a straight line is $y = mx + c$, then the equation of the ramp is $y = -[A/(T/2)]t + 2A$. Thus the waveform is described by

$$y = \frac{A}{T/2} t \text{ for } 0 \le t < T/2$$
$$y = -\frac{A}{T/2} t + 2A \text{ for } T/2 \le t < T, \text{ period } T$$

Example

Sketch the graph of the following waveform:

$$y = 0 \text{ for } 0 \le t < T/2$$
$$y = \sin t \text{ for } T/2 \le t < T, \text{ period } T$$

The waveform has a zero value for y over the first half period and

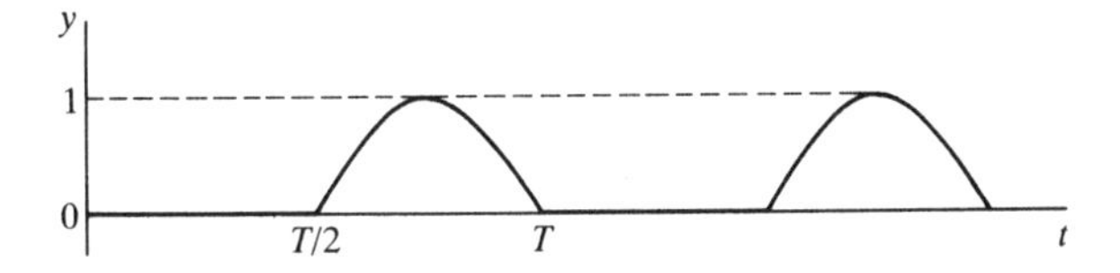

Fig. 1.8 Example

a sine wave of amplitude 1 over the second. The waveform is thus a half-wave rectified signal of the form shown in figure 1.8

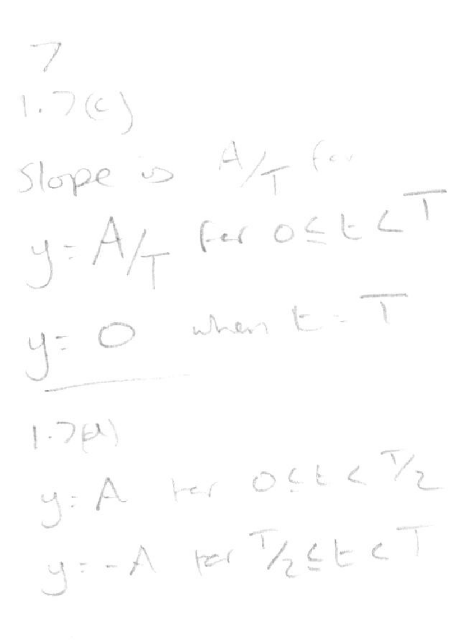

Review problems

7 Describe the waveforms in figure 1.7(c) and 1.7(d) by mathematical expressions.

8 Sketch graphs of the following waveforms:
(a) $y = A$ for $0 \leq t < T/2$, $y = -A/2$ for $T/2 \leq t < T$,
(b) $y = 2 \sin t$ for $0 \leq t < T/2$, $y = 2 \sin t$ for $T/2 \leq t < T$,
(c) $y = 0$ for $0 \leq t < 2$, $y = t$ for $2 \leq t < 3$, period = 3,
(d) $y = 2t$ for $0 \leq t < 1$, $y = 4 - 2t$ for $1 \leq t < 2$, period = 2.

9 Describe the waveforms shown in figure 1.9 by mathematical expressions.

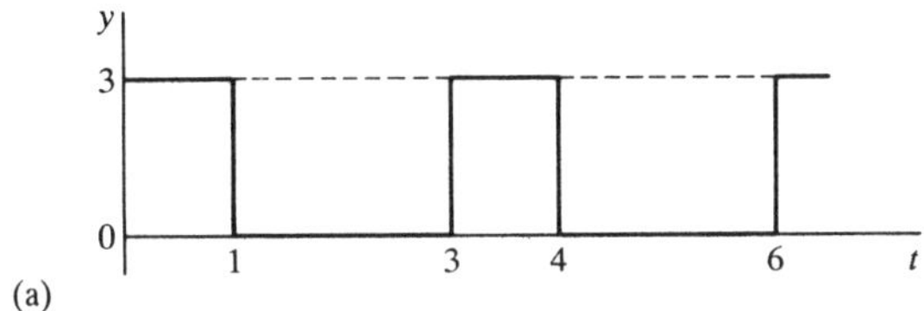

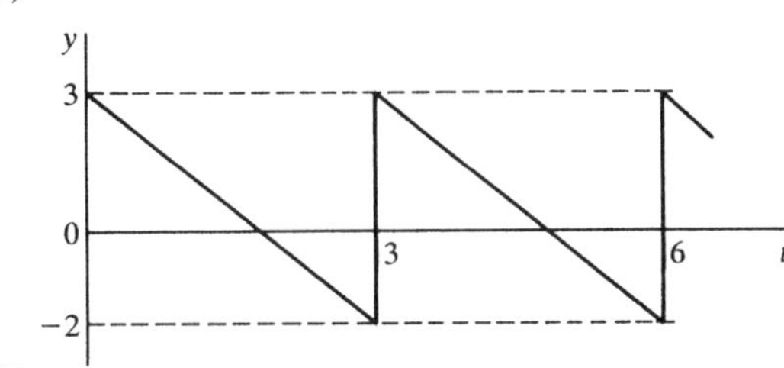

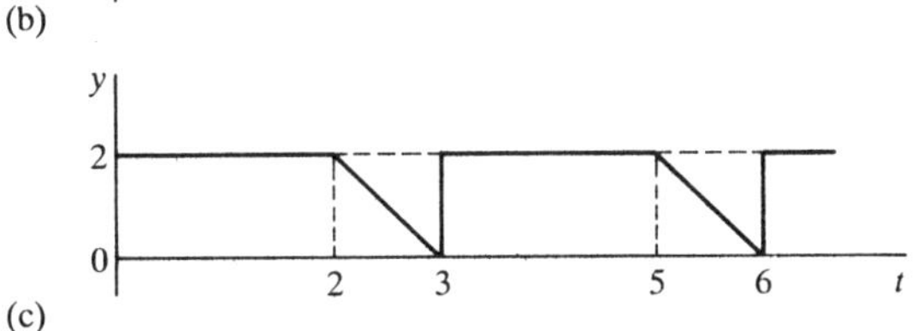

Fig. 1.9 Problem 9

Further problems

10 Sketch graphs, for one cycle, corresponding to:
(a) $y = 1 \sin \theta$, (b) $y = 2 \cos \theta$

11 Determine the values of the waveform given by $y = 4 \sin \omega t$ when (a) $\omega t = 0$, (b) $\omega t = \pi/3$, (c) $\omega t = \pi/2$, (d) $\omega t = 2\pi/3$, (e) $\omega t = \pi$, (f) $\omega t = 5\pi/3$, (g) $\omega t = 7\pi/3$.

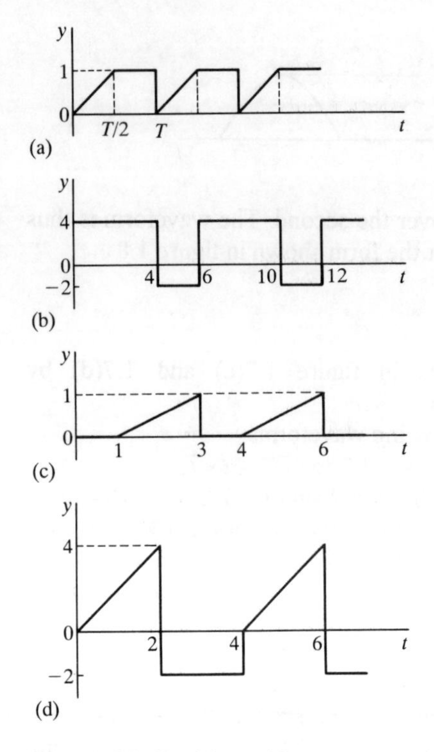

Fig. 1.10 Problem 16

12 Determine the values of the waveform given by $y = 5 \sin 10t$ when (a) $t = 0.1$ s, (b) $t = 0.2$ s, (c) $t = 0.3$ s.

13 Determine the values of y for the waveform given by the equation $y = 10 \sin (50t + \pi/3)$ when: (a) $t = 0$, (b) $t = 0.01$ s, (c) $t = 0.02$ s.

14 If the frequency of the fundamental is 20 Hz, what will be the frequencies of the second and third harmonics?

15 If a fundamental waveform is described by $y = 100 \sin 50t$, what will be the equations of the third and fifth harmonics?

16 Describe by mathematical expressions the waveforms for which the graphs are given in figure 1.10.

17 Sketch graphs of the following waveforms:
(a) $y = t$ for $0 \le t < 2$, $y = (10 - 2t)/3$ for $2 \le t < 5$,
(b) $y = \sin t$ for $0 \le t < 3$, $y = -2$ for $3 \le t < 4$,
(c) $y = 6 - 3t/4$ for $0 \le t < 8$, $y = 0$ for $8 \le t < 12$,
(d) $y = 2t$ for $0 \le t < 0.5$, $y = 2 - 2t$ for $0.5 \le t < 1$.

2 The Fourier series

2.1 Periodic functions

A *periodic function* is one for which the entire set of function values repeats itself at regular intervals; the time between successive repetitions being called the *periodic time*. Periodic functions often occur in engineering, e.g. current and voltage waveforms occur in electrical and electronic circuits. A simple waveform such as this might be the sinusoidal variation of current with time, i.e. the conventional alternating current. However, other periodic waveforms can occur, e.g. a square waveform or perhaps a distorted sinusoidal waveform. This chapter shows how we can represent such periodic functions, whatever their waveform. This involves the manipulation of trigonometric functions and integration, the reader might thus find the Appendix to this book of use in its review of these principles.

A common form of periodic function is that represented by

$$y = A \sin \omega t$$

(See chapter 1 for a discussion of this equation and the waveform it represents.) y is the value of the function at a time t and has started off at time $t = 0$ with a zero value. A is the amplitude, i.e. the maximum value of y. Such a function repeats itself every 360° or 2π radians. ω is the angular frequency and is equal to $2\pi f$ with f being the frequency of the waveform. If we doubled the frequency of the waveform then the equation would become

$$y = A \sin 2\omega t$$

Treble the frequency and we have

$$y = A \sin 3\omega t$$

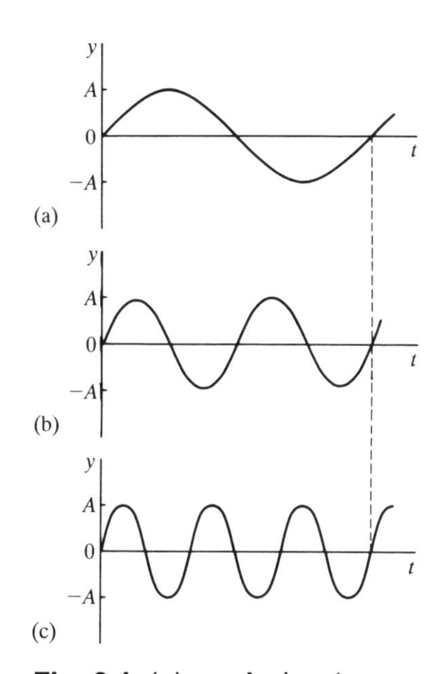

Fig. 2.1 (a) $y = A \sin \omega t$, (b) $y = A \sin 2\omega t$, (c) $y = A \sin 3\omega t$

Figure 2.1 shows graphs of the above three equations.

If the above functions had not started off with zero values at time $t = 0$ but with a phase angle ϕ then we might have, for the single, double and treble frequencies with different amplitudes and phase angles,

$$y = A_1 \sin(\omega t + \phi_1)$$

$$y = A_2 \sin(2\omega t + \phi_2)$$

$$y = A_3 \sin(3\omega t + \phi_3)$$

By adding together a number of periodic waveforms we can build up other periodic functions. Jean Baptiste Fourier (1768–1830) showed that a periodic function, whatever the waveform, can be built up from a series of sinusoidal waves of multiples of a basic frequency. Thus we can consider any periodic signal to be represented by a constant signal of size A_0, i.e. a d.c. term, plus sines of multiples of a basic frequency, each possibly having a different amplitude and phase angle.

$$y = A_0 + A_1 \sin(\omega t + \phi_1) + A_2 \sin(2\omega t + \phi_2) + A_3 \sin(3\omega t + \phi_3) + \ldots + A_n \sin(n\omega t + \phi_n) \quad [1]$$

This equation is the basis of what is known as the *Fourier series*. The term $A_1 \sin(\omega t + \phi_1)$ is the *first harmonic* or *fundamental mode*, the $A_2 \sin(2\omega t + \phi_2)$ the *second harmonic*, and so on to the $A_n \sin(n\omega t + \phi_n)$ term which is the *nth harmonic* (see section 1.2.2 for a discussion of harmonics).

Following on from the discussion in chapter 1 of the generation of sinusoidal waveforms by rotating radius arms, or phasors, we can consider equation [1] to be the build up of the periodic waveform by the algebraic addition of the projections of the radius arms rotating with angular velocities of 0, ω, 2ω, 3ω, ... $n\omega$.

Figure 2.2 shows how a waveform starting to approach that of a square waveform can be built up with the addition of the fundamental and the third harmonic, the amplitude of the third harmonic being one-third that of the fundamental. For such a waveform we have

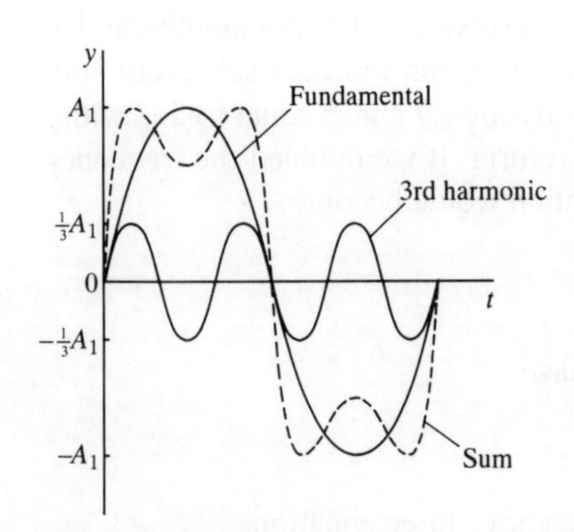

Fig. 2.2 $y = A_1 \sin \omega t + \frac{1}{3}A_1 \sin 3\omega t$

$$y = A_1 \sin \omega t + \tfrac{1}{3}A_1 \sin 3\omega t$$

A better approximation to a square waveform is given by adding higher odd harmonics with amplitudes which decrease in the way given by

$$y = A_1 \sin \omega t + \tfrac{1}{3}A_1 \sin 3\omega t + \tfrac{1}{5}A_1 \sin 5\omega t + \tfrac{1}{7}A_2 \sin 7\omega t + \ldots$$

Note that in the above discussions we have considered the Fourier series to be a series of sine waves. We could equally well have considered the series to be a series of cosine waves. A cosine wave is just a sine wave that started 90° or π/2 rad later, i.e. it starts off with the maximum amplitude at time $t = 0$ (see sections 1.2 and 1.2.1). The square wave could thus be expressed as

$$y_1 = A_1\cos(\omega t - 90°) + \tfrac{1}{3}A_1\cos(3\omega t - 90°) + \tfrac{1}{5}A_1\cos(5\omega t - 90°) + \tfrac{1}{7}A_1\cos(7\omega t - 90°) + \ldots$$

To illustrate this point, i.e. that a waveform can be described by a Fourier series provided we consider enough terms, consider another series. The series for an exponential is

$$e^x = 1 + x + \frac{x^2}{2!} + \frac{x^3}{3!} + \frac{x^4}{4!} + \frac{x^5}{5!} + \ldots$$

We can use this series to determine how the function e^x depends on x, in the same way as we can use the Fourier series to determine how y depends on the time t. If we consider a particular value of x, say $x = 1$, then

$$e^1 = 1 + 1 + 0.5 + 0.166\,67 + 0.041\,67 + 0.008\,33 + \ldots$$

If we only considered the first term in this series then a value for e^1 of 1 would be suggested, with two terms 2, with three terms 2.5, with four terms 2.666 67, with five terms 2.708 34, with six terms 2.716 67. If we consider yet more terms then in the limit we end up with 2.718 281 828 459 045 2.... Thus the more terms we consider the better the approximation. This is true with the Fourier series.

Review problems

1 Determine graphically the waveform generated by the following Fourier series:
(a) $y = 0.32 + 0.5 \sin \omega t - 0.21 \cos 2\omega t$,
(b) $y = 2 \sin \omega t + \cos 2\omega t$.
(Note that graphically means plotting the graphs for each of the separate elements in the series and then adding the ordinates of the graphs at specific times in order to determine the algebraic sum.)

2.1.1 Useful angle relationships

In working with the Fourier series the following are found to be useful relationships (see the note in section 1.2.1 regarding the use of degrees and radians in such expressions and the Appendix for further expressions):

$$\cos \omega t = \sin(\omega t + 90^\circ) = -\sin(\omega t - 90^\circ)$$

$$= \sin(\omega t + \pi/2) = -\sin(\omega t - \pi/2)$$

$$\sin \omega t = -\cos(\omega t + 90^\circ) = \cos(\omega t - 90^\circ)$$

$$= -\cos(\omega t + \pi/2) = \cos(\omega t - \pi/2)$$

$$\cos \omega t = -\cos(\omega t + 180^\circ) = -\cos(\omega t - 180^\circ)$$

$$= -\cos(\omega t + \pi) = -\cos(\omega t - \pi)$$

$$\sin \omega t = -\sin(\omega t + 180^\circ) = -\sin(\omega t - 180^\circ)$$

$$= -\sin(\omega t + \pi) = -\sin(\omega t - \pi)$$

A useful simplification which can sometimes be used is

$$A \cos(\omega t - \phi) = a \cos \omega t + b \sin \omega t \qquad [2]$$

This is obtained by writing

$$A \cos(\omega t - \phi) = A[\cos \omega t \cos \phi + \sin \omega t \sin \phi]$$

If we write $A \cos \phi = a$ and $A \sin \phi = b$ then equation [2] is obtained. These conditions then give

$$A^2 \cos^2 \phi + A^2 \sin^2 \phi = a^2 + b^2$$

and as $\cos^2 \phi + \sin^2 \phi = 1$ we then have

$$A = \sqrt{a^2 + b^2} \qquad [3]$$

Likewise we can write

$$A \cos(\omega t + \phi) = a \cos \omega t - b \sin \omega t \qquad [4]$$

with $A = \sqrt{a^2 + b^2}$. Also we have, for the sine relationships,

$$A \sin(\omega t + \phi) = a \sin \omega t + b \cos \omega t \qquad [5]$$

and

$$A \sin(\omega t - \phi) = a \sin \omega t - b \cos \omega t$$

with $a = A \cos \phi$ and $b = A \sin \phi$ and so $A = \sqrt{a^2 + b^2}$.

Example

If $y = 2 \sin 3t + 4 \cos 3t$, express y as a single cosine or sine.

Using equation [2] we can write

$$A \cos(\omega t - \phi) = a \cos \omega t + b \sin \omega t$$

with $A = \sqrt{a^2 + b^2} = \sqrt{4^2 + 2^2} = 4.5$. We can use $a = A \cos\phi$ to obtain ϕ as $\cos^{-1}(4/4.5) = 27° = 0.48$ rad. Thus

$$y = 4.5 \cos(3t - 27°) = 4.5 \cos(3t - 0.48)$$

Alternatively, we could have used equation [5]

$$A \sin(\omega t + \phi) = a \sin \omega t + b \cos \omega t$$

to have obtained

$$y = 4.5 \sin(3t + 64°) = 4.5 \sin(3t + 1.1)$$

since $A = \sqrt{a^2 + b^2} = \sqrt{4^2 + 2^2} = 4.5$ and, using $a = A \cos\phi$, then $\phi = \cos^{-1}(2/4.5) = 64° = 1.1$ rad.

Review problems

2 Express $y = 10 \sin 4t$ as a cosine.
3 Express $y = 2 \sin 5t + 3 \cos 5t$ as a single cosine or sine.

2.1.2 The frequency spectrum

When a waveform has been broken down into its Fourier components, a graph of the amplitudes of each of the sinusoidal waveforms plotted against the frequency is termed the *amplitude spectrum*. A plot of the phases of each of these plotted against the frequency is the *phase spectrum*. The two then constitute the *frequency spectrum* for the waveform.

Note that it is important to state for the phase spectrum whether the phases are with reference to a rotating radius arm, termed a phasor, generating the wave and starting off with $y = 0$ at time $t = 0$, i.e. generating sine waves, or one which is starting off with y as the amplitude at time $t = 0$, i.e. generating cosine waves (see chapter 1). Depending on whether the sine or cosine version is chosen, then the phases will differ by 90°.

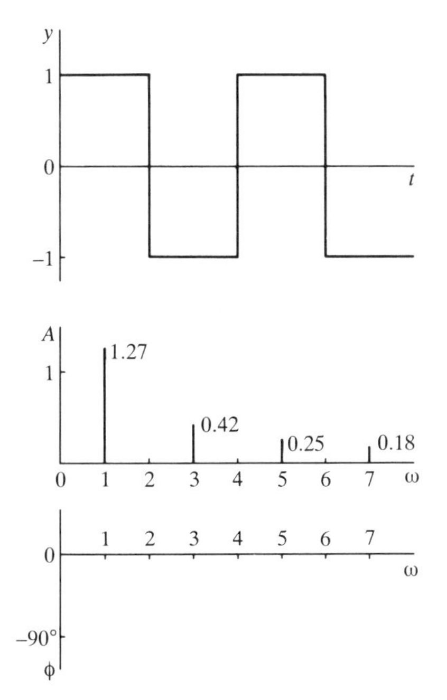

Fig. 2.3 A frequency spectrum

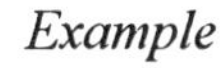

Example

Figure 2.3 shows the frequency spectrum for a square waveform when the phases have been measured relative to a phasor which has $y = 0$ at time $t = 0$. Explain the significance of the data and represent the waveform as a Fourier series.

The amplitude spectrum shows that the square waveform can be considered to be made up of sinusoidal waveforms of amplitude 1.27 at the fundamental frequency, 0.42 at the third harmonic, 0.25 at the fifth harmonic and 0.18 at the seventh harmonic. Each of the sinusoidal waveforms has a phase of 0°. Thus we can represent the square waveform as the Fourier series

$$y = 1.27 \sin \omega t + 0.42 \sin 3\omega t + 0.25 \sin 5\omega t + 0.18 \sin 7\omega t$$

Note that if the phase spectrum had been stated in terms of cosines then the phases of all the components would have been −90° and so the result would have been expressed as

$$y = 1.27 \cos(\omega t - 90°) + 0.42 \cos(3\omega t - 90°) + 0.25 \cos(5\omega t - 90°) + 0.18 \cos(7\omega t - 90°)$$

or, in the more consistent form when both terms in each bracket are in radians,

$$y = 1.27 \cos(\omega t - \pi/2) + 0.42 \cos(3\omega t - \pi/2) + 0.25 \cos(5\omega t - \pi/2) + 0.18 \cos(7\omega t - \pi/2)$$

All these equations describe the same waveform.

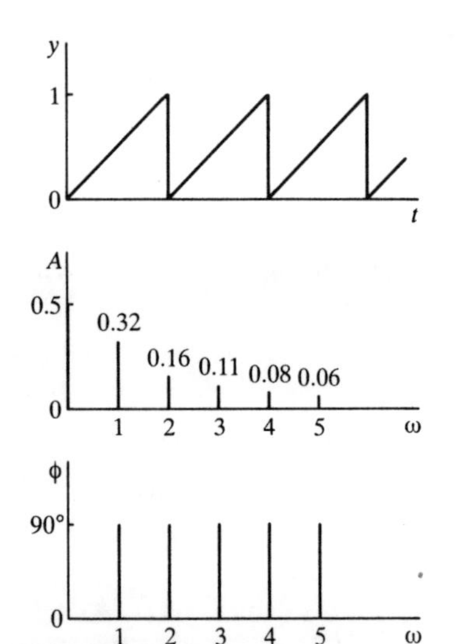

Fig. 2.4 Sawtooth waveform

Review problems

4 Figure 2.4 shows the frequency spectrum for a sawtooth waveform with the phases being measured relative to y equal to the amplitude at time $t = 0$. Represent the waveform as a Fourier series.

5 Draw the amplitude and phase spectra for a waveform which gives the Fourier series

$$y = 2 + 3 \sin \omega t + 5 \cos 2\omega t + 7 \sin 3\omega t$$

For the phase spectrum state the phasor used as the reference for zero phase.

2.2 The Fourier series

In general, a periodic function can be expressed as the sum of a series of sinusoidal waves of different amplitudes, phases and frequencies (equation [1]).

$$y = A_0 + A_1 \sin(\omega t + \phi_1) + A_2 \sin(2\omega t + \phi_2) + A_3 \sin(3\omega t + \phi_3) + \ldots + A_n \sin(n\omega t + \phi_n)$$

This is often more concisely expressed as

$$y = A_0 + \sum_{n=1}^{\infty} A_n \sin(n\omega t + \phi_n) \qquad [6]$$

There is however an alternative way of expressing the above relationship. Since

$$A_n \sin(n\omega t + \phi_n) = A_n \sin\phi_n \cos n\omega t + A_n \cos\phi_n \sin n\omega t$$

and if we represent the non-time varying terms $A_n \sin\phi_n$ and $A_n \cos\phi_n$ by constants a_n and b_n then

$$A_n \sin(n\omega t + \phi_n) = a_n \cos n\omega t + b_n \sin n\omega t$$

and equation [1] can be written as

$$y = \tfrac{1}{2}a_0 + a_1 \cos\omega t + a_2 \cos 2\omega t + \ldots + a_n \cos n\omega t + b_1 \sin\omega t + b_2 \sin 2\omega t + \ldots + b_n \sin n\omega t \qquad [7]$$

with, for convenience (see later), a_0 being taken as $2A_0$. These terms can be written in a more concise form as

$$y = \tfrac{1}{2}a_0 + \sum_{n=1}^{\infty} a_n \cos n\omega t + \sum_{n=1}^{\infty} b_n \sin n\omega t \qquad [8]$$

The a and b terms are called the *Fourier coefficients*. Thus the expression of a single harmonic by a single sinusoid with a phase angle can be replaced by the equivalent expression of the sum of a cosine and sine of the harmonic with no phase angle.

Since we have $a_n = A_n \sin\phi_n$ and $b_n = A_n \cos\phi_n$ then

$$a_n^2 + b_n^2 = A_n^2 \sin^2\phi_n + A_n^2 \cos^2\phi_n$$

and thus

$$A_n = \sqrt{(a_n^2 + b_n^2)} \qquad [9]$$

We also have

$$\frac{a_n}{b_n} = \frac{A_n \sin\phi_n}{A_n \cos\phi_n}$$

and hence

$$\phi_n = \tan^{-1}\left(\frac{a_n}{b_n}\right) \qquad [10]$$

Tan^{-1} means that ϕ_n is the angle whose tangent is b_n/a_n. It is termed an inverse trignometric function. As an illustration, we might write tan 45° = 1 or 45° = $\tan^{-1} 1$. It does *not* mean that we have $1/\tan(b_n/a_n)$. To avoid this confusion it is sometimes written as $\arctan(b_n/a_n)$.

Note that the Fourier series is often written as the sum of a series of cosine terms (rather than the sine terms used in equation [1]), i.e.

$$y = A_0 + A_1\cos(\omega t + \phi_1) + A_2\cos(2\omega t + \phi_2) + A_3\cos(3\omega t + \phi_2) + \ldots + A_n\cos(n\omega t + \phi_n) \qquad [11]$$

or, in a more concise form

$$y = A_0 + \sum_{n=1}^{\infty} A_n \cos(n\omega t + \phi_n) \qquad [12]$$

We can then use the relationship

$$A_n\cos(n\omega t + \phi) = A_n\cos\phi\cos n\omega t - A_n\sin\phi\sin n\omega t$$

with $a_n = A_n \cos\phi_n$ and $b_n = -A_n \sin\phi_n$ to give equation [8], namely

$$y = \tfrac{1}{2}a_0 + \sum_{n=1}^{\infty} a_n \cos n\omega t + \sum_{n=1}^{\infty} b_n \sin n\omega t$$

We then have

$$A_n = \sqrt{(a_n^2 + b_n^2)} \qquad [13]$$

$$\phi = \tan^{-1}\left(\frac{-b_n}{a_n}\right) \qquad [14]$$

The reason for the difference in the phases given by equations [14] and [10] is that, for equation [10], the phases are measured relative to $y = 0$ at $t = 0$ and for equation [14] relative to y as the maximum value at $t = 0$, there being a 90° difference between these two positions.

Example

One of the constituent waveforms in the spectrum of a waveform is $10\cos(100t + \pi/6)$ or $10\cos(100t + 30°)$. What would be the coefficients of the terms representing this in the Fourier series when expressed in the form of cosines and sines, i.e. in the form given by equation [8]?

Taking the phase measured relative to y being the maximum value at $t = 0$, we have

$$a_n = A_n \cos\phi_n = 10\cos 30° = 8.7$$

$$b_n = -A_n \sin\phi_n = -10\sin 30° = -5.0$$

The term is thus $8.7 \cos 100t - 5.0 \sin 100t$.

If we wanted to take the phase relative to $y = 0$ at $t = 0$ then we can rewrite the waveform as $10\sin(100t + 120°)$. Then we have

$$a_n = A_n\cos\phi_n = 10\cos 120° = -5.0$$

$$b_n = -A_n\sin\phi_n = -10\sin 120° = 8.7$$

The term then is $-5.0 \cos 100t + 8.7 \sin 100t$.

Example

What is the amplitude and the phase of the constituent waveform at a frequency of 100 rad/s if the terms for that particular harmonic have Fourier coefficients of $a_n = 5$ and $b_n = -2$?

Expressing the phase as being relative to y having the maximum amplitude at $t = 0$, then using equation [13]

$$A_n = \sqrt{(a_n^2 + b_n^2)} = \sqrt{(25 + 4)} = 5.4$$

Using equation [14]

$$\phi_n = \tan^{-1}\left(\frac{-b_n}{a_n}\right) = \tan^{-1}\left(\frac{2}{5}\right) = 22° \text{ or } 0.38 \text{ rad}$$

The harmonic is thus $5.4\cos(100t + 22°)$ or $5.4 \cos(100t + 0.38)$.

Review problems

6 What are the amplitude and phase of a waveform expressed as a single sinusoid if $y = 0.5 \sin 20t + 1.5 \cos 20t$?

7 What are the amplitude and phase of a waveform expressed as a single sinusoid if $y = 3\cos t - 4\sin t$?

2.2.1 Validity of the Fourier series

The validity of a series to represent a function depends on the series converging. Thus, for example, using the binomial theorem we can write for some function y of x, i.e. $y = f(x)$,

$$\frac{1}{1-x} = (1-x)^{-1} = 1 + x + x^2 + x^3 + \dots$$

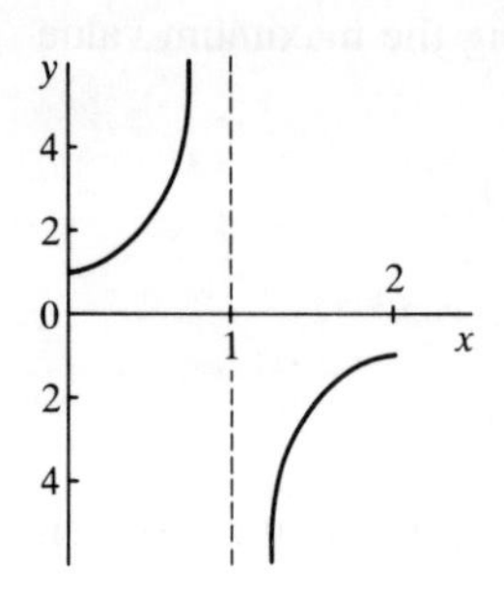

Fig. 2.5 $y = \dfrac{1}{1-x}$

This series will only converge if $|x| < 1$. Therefore this function of x will only have a finite value if $|x| < 1$. If we plotted out a graph of y against x (figure 2.5) we would have finite values for y when $|x| < 1$ but when $x = 1$ we would have an infinite value. We thus have a continuous graph either side of $x = 1$ but an infinite discontinuity at this point on the graph.

The validity of a Fourier series to represent a particular waveform, i.e. a particular function $y = f(t)$, is determined by what are called the *Dirichlet conditions*. These can be stated as:

1 For each value of t there is only one value of y.
2 y must be continuous or have a finite number of finite discontinuities within the periodic interval (see section 1.3).
3 y must be piecewise continuous.

These are the conditions that the Fourier series expansion of $f(t)$ converges to $f(t)$ at all points where $f(t)$ is continuous.

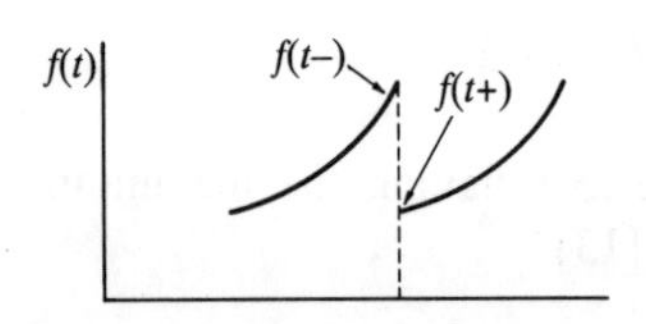

Fig. 2.6 A discontinuity

For a function that is piecewise continuous, the Fourier series converges to the value $f(t)$ at each point where the function is continuous and the value $\frac{1}{2}[f(t+) + f(t-)]$ at each point where it is discontinuous. $f(t+)$ is the value of the function immediately on the + side of the discontinuity and $f(t-)$ is the value on the − side of the discontinuity (figure 2.6).

For most cases encountered in engineering, the Fourier series is a valid representation.

Example

For the waveform shown in figure 2.7, to what values will the Fourier series converge at (a) $t = 1$, (b) $t = 2$, (c) $t = 3$?

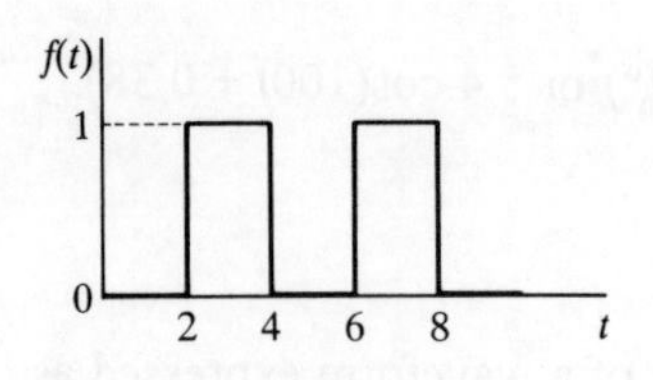

Fig. 2.7 Example

(a) For this time the function is continuous with $f(t) = 0$ and so the Fourier series will converge to 0.
(b) This is the time at which there is a discontinuity with $f(t)$ changing from 0 to 1. The Fourier series thus converges to the value $\frac{1}{2}(0 + 1) = \frac{1}{2}$.

(c) For this time the function is continuous with $f(t) = 1$ and so the Fourier series will converge to 1.

2.3 Finding the Fourier coefficients

Consider the Fourier series in the sine–cosine form (equation [7])

$$y = \tfrac{1}{2}a_0 + a_1\cos\omega t + a_2\cos 2\omega t + \ldots + a_n\cos n\omega t$$
$$+ b_1\sin\omega t + b_2\sin 2\omega t + \ldots\ b_n\sin n\omega t \qquad [15]$$

Now consider the effect of integrating both sides of the equation over one period T of the fundamental (see the Appendix for a revision of integration). The integral for each cosine and sine term will be the area under the graph of that expression for the time T. Therefore, since each sine and cosine terms covers a whole number of cycles in the time T, the negative parts of each cycle must cancel out the positive parts and so their integrals will be zero (see section 2.3.1). We can obtain this result by integrating. Thus

$$\int_{t_0}^{t_0+T} \cos\omega t = \left[\frac{1}{\omega}\sin\omega t\right]_{t_0}^{t_0+T}$$

The result is the difference between two sines which are T apart. Since T is the period, the answer is 0. A consequence of this is that the only term which is not zero when we integrate equation [15] is the integral of the a_0 term. Thus, integrating from some arbitrary time t_0 over one period T gives

$$\int_{t_0}^{t_0+T} y\,\mathrm{d}t = \int_{t_0}^{t_0+T} \tfrac{1}{2}a_0\,\mathrm{d}t = \tfrac{1}{2}a_0 T$$

Thus

$$a_0 = \frac{2}{T}\int_{t_0}^{t_0+T} y\,\mathrm{d}t \qquad [16]$$

We can obtain the a_1 term by multiplying equation [15] by $\cos\omega t$ and then integrating over one period. Thus equation [15] becomes

$$y\cos\omega t = \tfrac{1}{2}a_0\cos\omega t + a_1\cos\omega t\cos\omega t + a_2\cos\omega t\cos 2\omega t$$
$$+ \ldots + b_1\cos\omega t\sin\omega t + b_2\cos\omega t\sin 2\omega t + \ldots$$

$$= \tfrac{1}{2}a_0\cos\omega t + a_1\cos^2\omega t + a_2\cos\omega t\cos 2\omega t$$
$$+ \ldots + b_1\cos\omega t\sin\omega t + b_2\cos\omega t\sin 2\omega t + \ldots$$

The integration over a period T of all the terms involving $\sin\omega t$

and cos ωt will be zero. Thus we are only left with the $\cos^2 \omega t$ term and so

$$\int_{t_0}^{t_0+T} y \cos \omega t \, dt = \int_{t_0}^{t_0+T} a_1 \cos^2 \omega t \, dt$$

Since $\cos^2 A = \frac{1}{2}(\cos 2A + 1)$ (see the Appendix) then

$$\int_{t_0}^{t_0+T} y \cos \omega t \, dt = a_1 \int_{t_0}^{t_0+T} \tfrac{1}{2}(\cos 2\omega t + 1) \, dt$$

$$= a_1 \int_{t_0}^{t_0+T} \tfrac{1}{2} \cos 2\omega t \, dt + a_1 \int_{t_0}^{t_0+T} \tfrac{1}{2} \, dt$$

The integral of the cos $2\omega t$ term over a period will be zero. Thus

$$\int_{t_0}^{t_0+T} y \cos \omega t \, dt = \tfrac{1}{2} a_1 T$$

and so

$$a_1 = \frac{2}{T} \int_{t_0}^{t_0+T} y \cos \omega t \, dt \qquad [17]$$

In general, multiplying equation [15] by cos $n\omega t$ we obtain

$$a_n = \frac{2}{T} \int_{t_0}^{t_0+T} y \cos n\omega t \, dt \qquad [18]$$

Equation [18] gives, when $n = 0$, the equation for a_0, i.e. equation [16]. This would not have been the case if the first term in the Fourier series had been written as a_0 instead of $a_0/2$. This simplification is thus the reason for the 1/2 being used with a_0 in the defining equation for the series.

Multiplying equation [15] by sin ωt gives

$$y \sin \omega t = \tfrac{1}{2} a_0 \sin \omega t + a_1 \sin \omega t \cos \omega t + a_2 \sin \omega t \cos 2\omega t$$

$$+ \ldots + b_1 \sin \omega t \sin \omega t + b_2 \sin \omega t \sin 2\omega t + \ldots$$

$$= \tfrac{1}{2} a_0 \sin \omega t + a_1 \sin \omega t \cos \omega t + a_2 \sin \omega t \cos 2\omega t$$
$$+ \ldots + b_1 \sin^2 \omega t + b_2 \sin \omega t \sin 2\omega t + \ldots$$

The integration over a period T of all the terms involving sin ωt and cos ωt will be zero. Thus

$$\int_{t_0}^{t_0+T} y \sin \omega t \, dt = \int_{t_0}^{t_0+T} b_1 \sin^2 \omega t \, dt$$

Since $\sin^2 A = \frac{1}{2}(1 - \cos 2A)$ (see the Appendix) then

$$\int_{t_0}^{t_0+T} y \sin \omega t \, dt = \int_{t_0}^{t_0+T} b_1 \tfrac{1}{2}(1 - \cos 2\omega t) \, dt$$

$$= \int_{t_0}^{t_0+T} \tfrac{1}{2} b_1 \, dt - \int_{t_0}^{t_0+T} b_1 \cos 2\omega t \, dt$$

The integral of the cos $2\omega t$ term over a period will be zero. Thus

$$\int_{t_0}^{t_0+T} y \sin \omega t \, dt = \tfrac{1}{2} b_1 T$$

Thus

$$b_1 = \frac{2}{T} \int_{t_0}^{t_0+T} y \sin \omega t \, dt \qquad [19]$$

In general, multiplying equation [15] by sin $n\omega t$ gives

$$b_n = \frac{2}{T} \int_{t_0}^{t_0+T} y \sin n\omega t \, dt \qquad [20]$$

2.3.1 Useful integrals

In determining the Fourier coefficients, the following integrals were used (see the Appendix for a discussion of integrals). Note that the period $T = 2\pi/\omega$.

$$\int_{t_0}^{t_0+T} \cos n\omega t \, dt = 0 \text{ when } n \neq 0$$

$$= T \text{ when } n = 0$$

$$\int_{t_0}^{t_0+T} \sin n\omega t \, dt = 0 \text{ for all values of } n$$

$$\int_{t_0}^{t_0+T} \cos m\omega t \cos n\omega t \, dt = 0 \text{ when } m \neq n$$

$$= T/2 \text{ when } m = n \neq 0$$

$$\int_{t_0}^{t_0+T} \sin m\omega t \sin n\omega t \, dt = 0 \text{ when } m \neq n$$

$$= T/2 \text{ when } m = n \neq 0$$

$$\int_{t_0}^{t_0+T} \cos m\omega t \sin n\omega t \, dt = 0 \text{ for all values of } n \text{ and } m$$

The above are said to be the *orthogonal relationships* for the sine and cosine functions.

2.3.2 Period 2π

The Fourier series coefficients considered in section 2.3 have been for a waveform of period T. Calculations can, however, often be simplified if a period of 2π is considered. This means that the integrals can be taken between limits of 2π and 0, or −π and +π. Since $T = 2\pi/\omega$, this implies an angular frequency of 1 rad/s. Thus

$$a_n = \frac{1}{\pi}\int_0^{2\pi} y \cos nt \, dt$$

$$b_n = \frac{1}{\pi}\int_0^{2\pi} y \sin nt \, dt$$

The Fourier series is then given by

$$y = \tfrac{1}{2}a_0 + a_1 \cos t + a_2 \cos 2t + \ldots + a_n \cos nt$$
$$+ b_1 \sin t + b_2 \sin 2t + \ldots + b_n \sin nt$$

We can consider that a graph of y plotted against t with a period of 2π just represents a graph plotted on a different time scale to one for which the period is T. The coefficients and the form of the graph will be the same.

2.4 Fourier series for common waveforms

In this section a number of common waveforms are considered and the Fourier coefficients determined, using the equations developed in section 2.3. A period of T has been used but, to illustrate the effect of using a period of 2π, the rectangular waveform in section 2.4.1 is considered for both T and 2π.

2.4.1 Rectangular waveforms

Consider the rectangular waveform shown in figure 2.8. We can describe the waveform as

$$y = A \text{ for } 0 \le t < T/2$$
$$y = 0 \text{ for } T/2 \le t < T, \text{ period } T$$

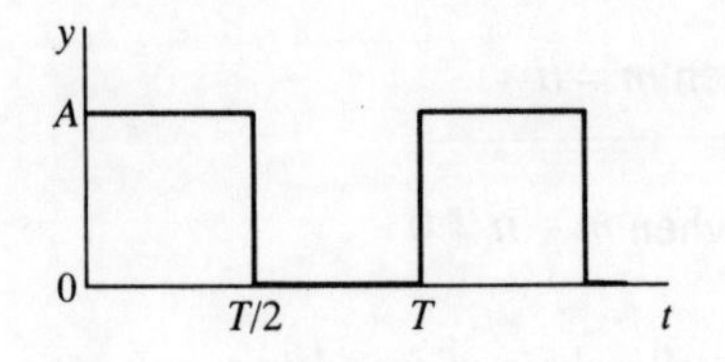

Fig. 2.8 Rectangular waveform

We can use equation [16] to obtain a_0. Thus

$$a_0 = \frac{2}{T}\int_0^T y \, dt$$

The integral is the area under the graph of y against t for the period T. Since this is $AT/2$ then $a_0 = A$.

We can use equation [18] to obtain a_n. Thus

$$a_n = \frac{2}{T}\int_0^T y \cos n\omega t \, dt$$

Since y has the value A only up to $T/2$ and is zero thereafter, we can write the above equation in two parts, namely

$$a_n = \frac{2}{T}\int_0^{T/2} A \cos n\omega t \, dt + \frac{2}{T}\int_{T/2}^{T} 0 \cos n\omega t \, dt$$

The value of the second integral is 0, thus

$$a_n = \frac{2}{T}\left[\frac{A}{n\omega}\sin n\omega t\right]_0^{T/2}$$

Since $\omega = 2\pi/T$ then we have, for the sine term, sin $2n\pi t/T$. Thus when $t = T/2$ we have sin $n\pi$ which is zero. Thus we have $a_n = 0$.

For the b_n terms we can use equation [20], namely

$$b_n = \frac{2}{T}\int_0^T y \sin n\omega t \, dt$$

Since we have $y = A$ from 0 to $T/2$ and then $y = 0$ for the remainder of the period, we can write

$$b_n = \frac{2}{T}\int_0^{T/2} A \sin n\omega t \, dt + \frac{2}{T}\int_{T/2}^{T} 0 \sin n\omega t \, dt$$

The value of the second integral is 0, thus

$$b_n = \frac{2}{T}\left[-\frac{A}{n\omega}\cos n\omega t\right]_0^{T/2}$$

Since $\omega = 2\pi/T$ and the cosine of 0 is 1, then we have

$$b_n = \frac{A}{\pi n}(1 - \cos n\pi)$$

Hence

$$b_1 = \frac{A}{\pi}(1 - \cos \pi) = \frac{2A}{\pi}$$

$$b_2 = \frac{A}{2\pi}(1 - \cos 2\pi) = 0$$

$$b_3 = \frac{A}{3\pi}(1 - \cos 3\pi) = \frac{2A}{3\pi}$$

Thus the Fourier series for the waveform can be written as

$$y = A\left(\frac{1}{2} + \frac{2}{\pi}\sin\omega t + \frac{2}{3\pi}\sin 3\omega t + \dots\right) \qquad [21]$$

We can determine the frequency spectrum by the use of equations [13] and [14], i.e. taking the Fourier series to be a sum of cosine terms (equation [11]) in order to define phase angles. Thus

$$A_n = \sqrt{(a_n^2 + b_n^2)}$$

and so, since $a_1 = 0$ and $b_1 = 2A/\pi$ we have $A_1 = 2A/\pi$. Since $a_2 = 0$ and $b_2 = 0$ then $A_2 = 0$. Since $a_3 = 0$ and $b_3 = 2A/3\pi$ then $A_3 = 2A/3\pi$.

$$\phi_n = \tan^{-1}\left(\frac{-b_n}{a_n}\right)$$

and so $\phi_1 = -\tan^{-1}\infty = -90°$. Likewise $\phi_3 = -90°$.

To show the effect of considering a period of 2π instead of T, consider the rectangular waveform to be determined by

$$y = A \text{ for } 0 \le t < \pi$$
$$y = 0 \text{ for } \pi \le t < 2\pi, \text{ period } 2\pi$$

The coefficients are given by

$$a_0 = \frac{1}{\pi}\int_0^{2\pi} y\,dt = \frac{1}{\pi}\int_0^{\pi} A\,dt = A$$

$$a_n = \frac{1}{\pi}\int_0^{2\pi} y\cos nt\,dt = \frac{1}{\pi}\int_0^{\pi} A\cos nt\,dt = \frac{1}{\pi}\left[\frac{A}{n}\sin nt\right]_0^{\pi} = 0$$

$$b_n = \frac{1}{\pi}\int_0^{2\pi} y\sin nt\,dt = \frac{1}{\pi}\int_0^{\pi} A\sin nt\,dt = \frac{A}{n\pi}(1 - \cos n\pi)$$

The coefficients are thus the same as obtained with period T. The Fourier series is thus

$$y = A\left(\frac{1}{2} + \frac{2}{\pi}\sin t + \frac{2}{3\pi}\sin 3t + \dots\right)$$

The only difference is that this series has $\omega = 1$.

Review problems

8 Derive the Fourier series for the rectangular waveform shown in figure 2.9.

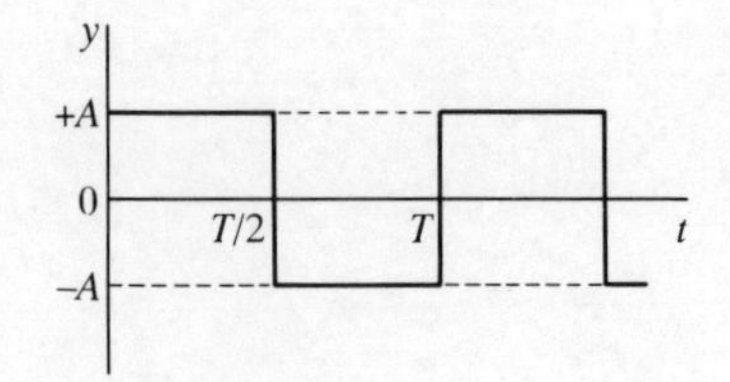

Fig. 2.9 Problem 8

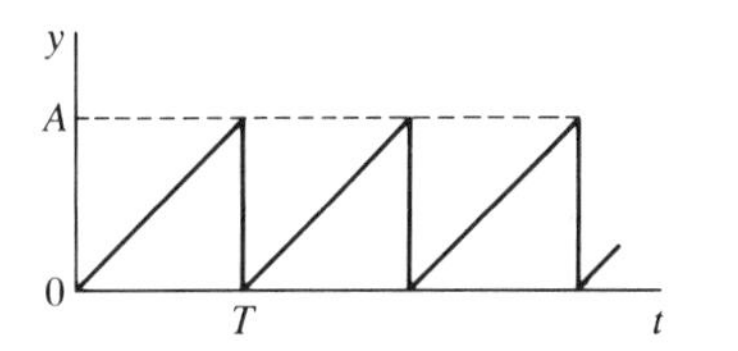

Fig. 2.10 Sawtooth waveform

2.4.2 Triangular waveforms

Consider the saw-tooth waveform shown in figure 2.10. It can be described by

$$y = At/T \text{ for } 0 \le t < T, \text{ period } T$$

We can use equation [16] to determine a_0. Thus

$$a_0 = \frac{2}{T}\int_0^T y\,\mathrm{d}t$$

The integral is the total area under the graph of y against t between 0 and time T. This is an area of $AT/2$. Hence $a_0 = A$.

We can use equation [18] to obtain a_n. Thus

$$a_n = \frac{2}{T}\int_0^T y \cos n\omega t\,\mathrm{d}t$$

Since $\omega = 2\pi/T$ and $y = At/T$ then

$$a_n = \frac{2}{T}\int_0^T \frac{At}{T}\cos\frac{2\pi nt}{T}\,\mathrm{d}t$$

Using integration by parts (see the Appendix), namely

$$\int u\,\mathrm{d}v = uv - \int v\,\mathrm{d}u$$

with $u = At/T$ and $\mathrm{d}v = \cos 2\pi nt/T\,\mathrm{d}t$ then

$$a_n = \frac{2}{T}\left[\frac{At}{2\pi n}\sin\frac{2\pi nt}{T} + \frac{At}{4\pi^2 n^2}\cos\frac{2\pi nt}{T}\right]_0^T$$

$$= \frac{2A}{T}\left[\frac{T}{4\pi^2 n^2} - \frac{T}{4\pi^2 n^2}\right] = 0$$

The values of b_n can be found by means of equation [20]. Thus

$$b_n = \frac{2}{T}\int_0^T y \sin n\omega t\,\mathrm{d}t$$

$$= \frac{2}{T}\int_0^T \frac{At}{T}\sin\frac{2\pi nt}{T}\,\mathrm{d}t$$

Integration by parts, with $u = At/T$ and $\mathrm{d}v = 2\pi nt/T\,\mathrm{d}t$, gives

$$b_n = \frac{2}{T}\left[-\frac{At}{2\pi n}\cos\frac{2\pi nt}{T} + \frac{At}{4\pi^2 n^2}\sin\frac{2\pi nt}{T}\right]_0^T$$

$$= \frac{2A}{T}\left[-\frac{T}{2\pi n}\right]_0^T = -\frac{A}{\pi n}$$

The Fourier series for the saw-tooth waveform is thus

$$y = \frac{A}{2} - \frac{A}{\pi}\sin\omega t - \frac{A}{2\pi}\sin 2\omega t - \frac{A}{3\pi}\sin 3\omega t - \dots \qquad [22]$$

We can determine the frequency spectrum by the use of equations [13] and [14], i.e. taking the Fourier series to be a sum of cosine terms (equation [11]) in order to define phase angles. Thus

$$A_n = \sqrt{(a_n^2 + b_n^2)}$$

Thus, since $a_n = 0$ then $A_n = A/\pi n$.

$$\phi_n = \tan^{-1}\left(\frac{-b_n}{a_n}\right)$$

and so $\phi_n = \tan^{-1}\infty = 90°$.

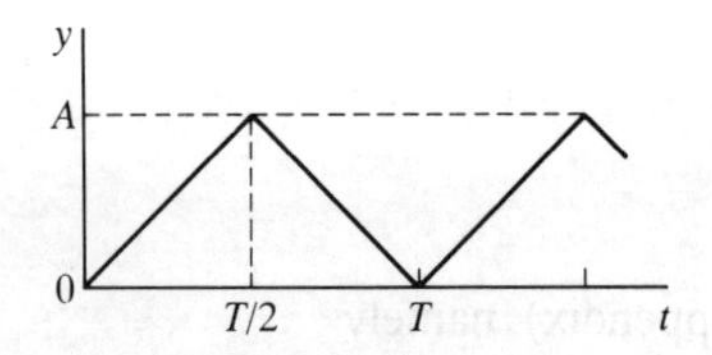

Fig. 2.11 Problem 9

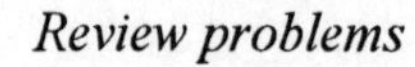

Review problems

9 Determine the Fourier series for the waveform given in figure 2.11.

2.4.3 Rectified sinusoid waveforms

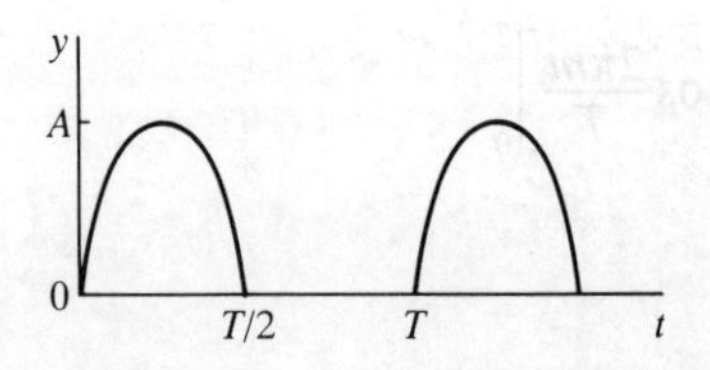

Fig. 2.12 Half-wave rectified sinusoid

Consider the half-wave rectified sinusoid shown in figure 2.12. It can be described by

$$y = A\sin\omega t = A\sin 2\pi t/T \text{ for } 0 \le t < T/2$$
$$y = 0 \text{ for } T/2 \le t < T, \text{ period } T$$

We can use equation [16] to determine a_0. Thus

$$a_0 = \frac{2}{T}\int_0^T y\,dt$$

The integral is the area under the graph. The total area under the graph between 0 and T is AT/π. Thus $a_0 = 2A/\pi$.

We can use equation [18] to obtain a_n. Thus

$$a_n = \frac{2}{T}\int_0^T y\cos n\omega t\,dt$$

Since $\omega = 2\pi/T$ and $y = A\sin 2\pi t/T$ for t between 0 and $T/2$ and $y = 0$ between $T/2$ and T, then

$$a_n = \frac{2}{T}\int_0^{T/2} A \sin\frac{2\pi t}{T}\cos\frac{2\pi nt}{T}\,dt + \frac{2}{T}\int_0^{T} 0\cos n\omega t\,dt$$

The second integral is thus 0. We can rewrite the first integral using the equation $2\sin A\cos B = \sin(A+B) + \sin(A-B)$ (see the Appendix). Then

$$a_n = \frac{2}{T}\int_0^{T/2} \frac{A}{2}\left[\sin\frac{2\pi}{T}(1+n)t + \sin\frac{2\pi}{T}(1-n)t\right]dt$$

When $n = 1$ this becomes

$$a_1 = \frac{2}{T}\int_0^{T/2} \frac{A}{2}\sin\frac{2\pi}{T}(1+1)t\,dt$$

$$= \frac{A}{T}\left[\frac{-\cos(4\pi t/T)}{(4\pi/T)}\right]_0^{T/2} = 0$$

For $n = 2, 3, 4$, etc. the integration gives

$$a_n = \frac{A}{T}\left[-\frac{\cos 2\pi(1+n)t/T}{2\pi(1+n)/T} - \frac{\cos 2\pi(1-n)t/T}{2\pi(1-n)/T}\right]_0^{T/2}$$

For $t = 0$ we have the cosines terms both equal to 1. For even values of n we have $\cos\pi(1+n) = -1$ and $\cos\pi(1-n) = -1$. Hence, for even values of n,

$$a_n = \frac{A}{T}\left[\frac{2}{2\pi(1+n)/T} + \frac{2}{2\pi(1-n)/T}\right]$$

$$= A\left[\frac{(1-n)+(1+n)}{\pi(1+n)(1-n)}\right]$$

$$= \frac{2A}{\pi(1-n^2)}$$

For $n = 3, 5, 7$, etc. then $\cos\pi(1+n) = 1$ and $\cos\pi(1-n) = 1$. Thus for these values of n we have $a_n = 0$.

The values of b_n can be found by equation [20].

$$b_n = \frac{2}{T}\int_0^{T} y\sin n\omega t\,dt$$

$$= \frac{2}{T}\int_0^{T/2} A\sin\frac{2\pi t}{T}\sin\frac{2\pi nt}{T}\,dt$$

$$= \frac{2}{T}\int_0^{T/2} \frac{A}{2}\left[\cos\frac{2\pi}{T}(1-n)t - \cos\frac{2\pi}{T}(1+n)t\right]dt$$

For $n = 1$ we have

$$b_1 = \frac{A}{T}\int_0^{T/2}\left[1 - \cos\frac{4\pi t}{T}\right]dt$$

$$= \frac{A}{T}\left[t - \frac{\sin 4\pi t/T}{4\pi/T}\right]_0^{T/2} = \frac{A}{2}$$

For $n = 2, 3, 4$, etc then

$$b_n = \frac{A}{T}\left[\frac{\sin 2\pi(1-n)t/T}{2\pi(1-n)/T} - \frac{\sin 2\pi(1+n)t/T}{2\pi(1+n)/T}\right]_0^{T/2}$$

Since $\sin \pi(1 - n)$ and $\sin \pi(1 + n)$ are both zero, for $n = 2, 3, 4$, etc we have $b_n = 0$.

The Fourier series for this half-wave rectified sinusoidal waveform is thus

$$y = \frac{A}{\pi} - \frac{2A}{3\pi}\cos 2\omega t - \frac{2A}{15\pi}\cos 4\omega t + \ldots + \frac{A}{2}\sin \omega t \qquad [23]$$

We can determine the frequency spectrum by the use of equations [13] and [14], i.e. taking the Fourier series to be a sum of cosine terms (equation [11]) in order to define phase angles. Thus

$$A_n = \sqrt{(a_n^2 + b_n^2)}$$

and so, for even values of n when we have a value for a_n but no value for b_n, we have

$$A_n = \frac{2A}{\pi(n^2 - 1)}$$

For $n = 1$ we have $a_1 = 0$ and so $A_1 = A/2$.

$$\phi_n = \tan^{-1}\left(\frac{-b_n}{a_n}\right)$$

Thus, for even values of n, we have $\phi_n = -\tan^{-1}0 = 180°$ and for $n = 1$ we have $\phi_1 = -90°$.

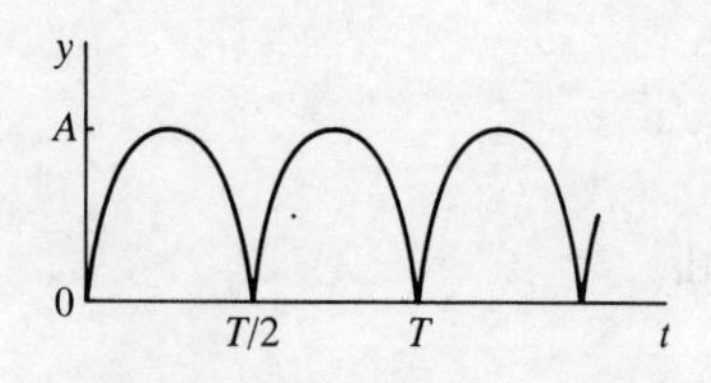

Fig. 2.13 Full-wave rectified sinusoid

Review problems

10 Determine the Fourier series for the full-wave rectified sinusoid shown in figure 2.13.

2.4.4 Commonly encountered waveforms

Table 2.1 shows the Fourier coefficients and frequency spectrum terms for commonly encountered waveforms. The phase angles have been given on the basis that the Fourier series is expressed in terms of cosines, i.e. equation [11]. When expressed on the basis of sines, i.e. equation [6], then 90° should be added to the phase angles quoted.

If a period of 2π, rather than T, is used then ω has the value of 1. Such a simplification reduces the amount of mathematical manipulation in deriving the coefficients. The results obtained by using this period of 2π are equally applicable to periods of T since, in effect, the unit of the angular frequency has been adjusted to a different scale. The values of the coefficients are the same.

2.4.5 Origin shifts

The Fourier series for the rectangular waveform in figure 2.14(a) is, with a period of 2π and amplitude 1,

$$y = f(t) = \frac{4}{\pi}\left(\sin t + \frac{1}{3}\sin 3t + \frac{1}{5}\sin 5t + \ldots\right)$$

Now consider what happens if the time origin is moved to the right by $\pi/2$ to give the rectangular waveform shown in figure 2.14(b). The Fourier series is now

$$y = f(t) = \frac{4}{\pi}\left[\sin\left(t + \frac{\pi}{2}\right) + \frac{1}{3}\sin 3\left(t + \frac{\pi}{2}\right) + \ldots\right]$$

$$= \frac{4}{\pi}\left(\cos t - \frac{1}{3}\cos 3t + \frac{1}{5}\cos 5t + \ldots\right)$$

In shifting the origin to the right by a time of $\pi/2$ all we have done is replace t by $(t + \pi/2)$.

In general, shifting the time origin to the right by θ means that t is replaced by $(t + \theta)$. Shifting to the left by θ means t is replaced by $(t - \theta)$. Since, for example (see the Appendix),

$$\cos(t - \theta) = \cos t \cos\theta + \sin t \sin\theta$$

and

$$\sin(t - \theta) = \sin t \cos\theta - \cos t \sin\theta$$

then it is apparent that for a function which gave a Fourier series with just cosine or sine terms that an origin shift may lead to a series with both cosine and sine terms.

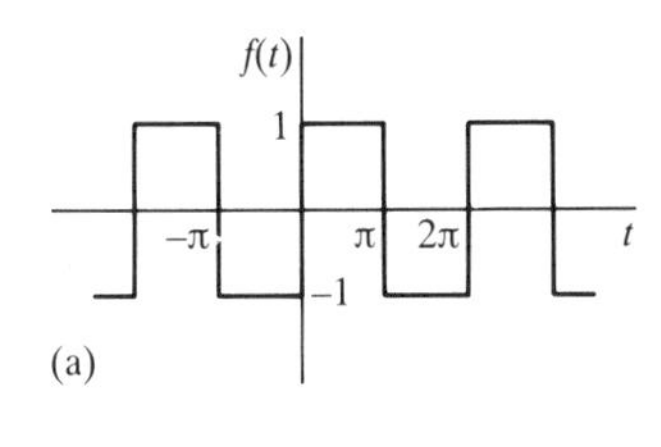

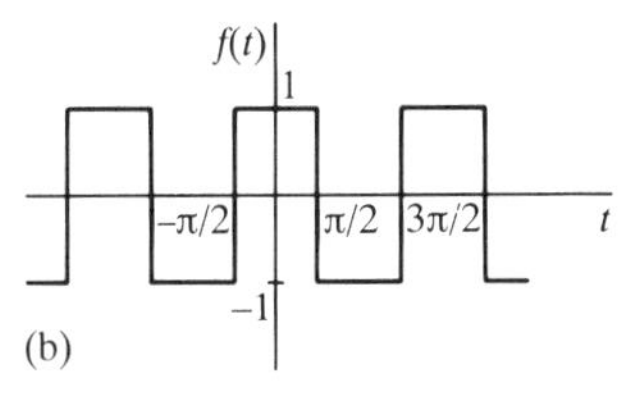

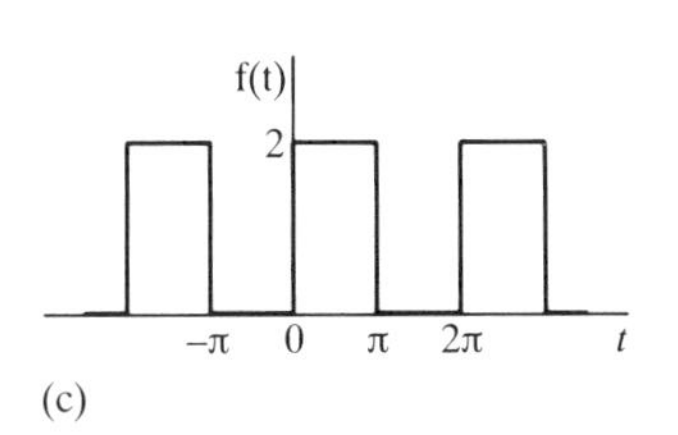

Fig. 2.14 Origin shifts

Table 2.1 Fourier coefficients and frequency spectrum

Waveform	Coefficients and frequency spectrum
1. Pulses 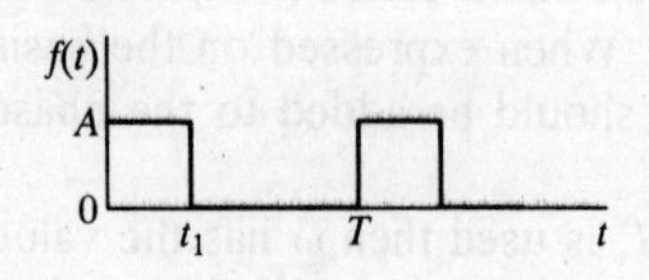 	$a_0 = \frac{2At_1}{T}$ $a_n = \frac{A}{\pi n} \sin \frac{2\pi n t_1}{T}$ $b_n = \frac{A}{\pi n}\left(1 - \cos \frac{2\pi n t_1}{T}\right)$ $A_0 = \frac{2At_1}{T}$ $A_n = \frac{A}{\pi n}\sqrt{\left(2 - 2\cos \frac{2\pi n t_1}{T}\right)}$ $\phi_n = -\tan^{-1}\left(\frac{1 - \cos 2\pi n t_1/T}{\sin 2\pi n t_1/T}\right)$
2. Rectangular 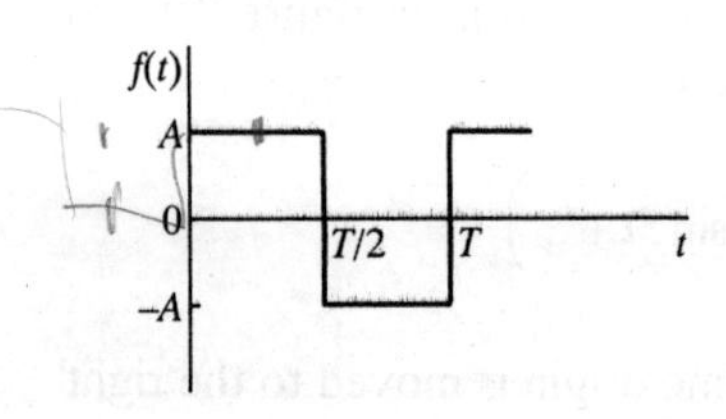 	$a_0 = 0$ $a_n = 0$ $b_n = \frac{4A}{\pi n}$ for $n = 1, 3, 5, \ldots$ $b_n = 0$ for $n = 2, 4, 6, \ldots$ $A_0 = 0$ $A_n = \frac{4A}{\pi n}$ for $n = 1, 3, 5, \ldots$ $\phi_n = -90^\circ$ for $n = 1, 3, 5, ..$
3. Sawtooth 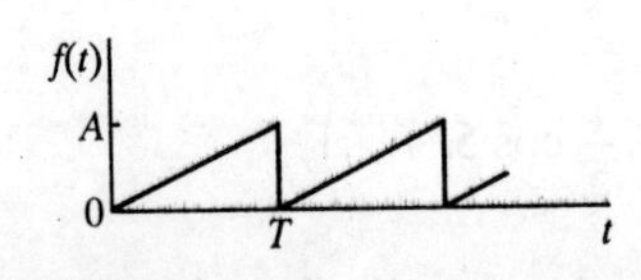 	$a_0 = A$ $a_n = 0$ $b_n = -\frac{A}{\pi n}$ $A_0 = A$ $A_n = \frac{A}{\pi n}$ $\phi_n = 90^\circ$
4. Triangular 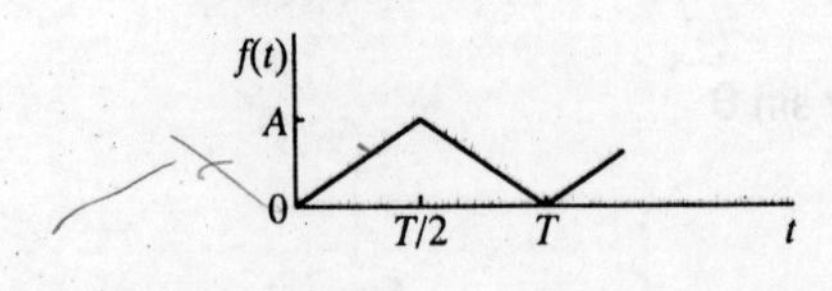 	$a_0 = A$ $a_n = -\frac{4A}{\pi^2 n^2}$ for $n = 1, 3, 5, \ldots$ $a_n = 0$ for $n = 2, 4, 6, \ldots$ $b_n = 0$ $A_0 = A$ $A_n = \frac{4A}{\pi^2 n^2}$ for $n = 1, 3, 5, \ldots$ $\phi_n = -180^\circ$ for $n = 1, 3, 5, \ldots$

5. Half-wave rectified sinusoid

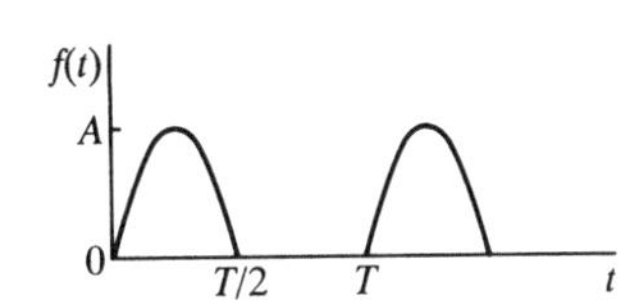

$$a_0 = \frac{2A}{\pi}$$
$$a_n = \frac{2A}{\pi(1-n^2)} \text{ for } n = 2, 4, 6, \ldots$$
$$a_n = 0 \text{ for } n = 1, 3, 5, \ldots$$
$$b_1 = \frac{A}{2}$$
$$b_n = 0 \text{ for } n = 2, 3, 4, 5, \ldots$$
$$A_0 = \frac{2A}{\pi}$$
$$A_n = \frac{2A}{\pi(n^2-1)} \text{ for } n = 2, 4, 6, \ldots$$
$$A_1 = \frac{A}{2}$$
$$\phi_1 = -90^\circ$$
$$\phi_n = 180^\circ \text{ for } n = 2, 4, 6, \ldots$$

6. Full-wave rectified sinusoid

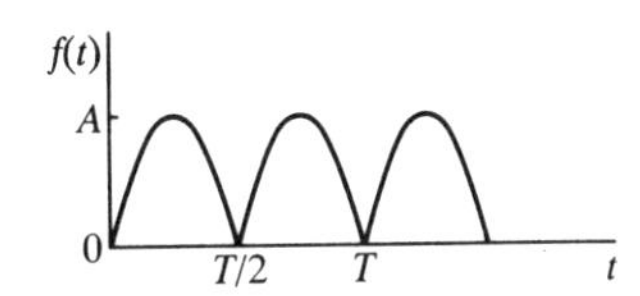

$$a_0 = \frac{4A}{\pi}$$
$$a_n = \frac{2A}{\pi(1-4n^2)}$$
$$b_n = 0$$
$$A_0 = \frac{4A}{\pi}$$
$$A_n = \frac{4A}{\pi(1-4n^2)}$$
$$\phi_n = 180^\circ$$

Now consider the rectangular waveform in figure 2.14(a) being shifted to give a new function origin, as in figure 2.14(c). We can consider the waveform in figure 2.14(c) to be that in figure 2.14(a) plus a constant signal of $f(t) = +1$. Hence the Fourier series is

$$y = f(t) = 1 + \frac{4}{\pi}\left(\sin t + \frac{1}{3}\sin 3t + \frac{1}{5}\sin 5t + \ldots\right)$$

Review problems

11 The Fourier series for a triangular waveform is given by

$$y = \frac{8}{\pi^2}\left(\sin t - \frac{1}{9}\sin 3t + \frac{1}{25}\sin 5t - \ldots\right)$$

Hence obtain the Fourier series for
(a) the waveform shifted to the right by $\pi/2$,
(b) the waveform shifted to the right by $\pi/2$ and upwards by 1.

2.5 Series

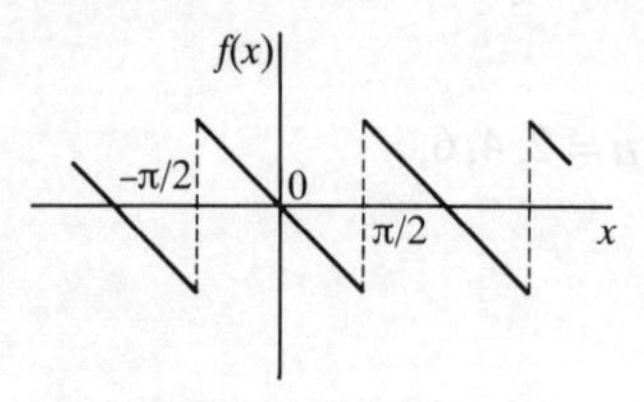

Fig. 2.15 Series values

Other series can be obtained from Fourier series by giving particular values to the variable. For example, the function shown in figure 2.15 has the Fourier series

$$y = -\sin 2x + \tfrac{1}{2}\sin 4x - \tfrac{1}{3}\sin 6x + \tfrac{1}{4}\sin 8x + \ldots$$

This function is continuous from 0 to $-\pi/2$. Thus it is continuous at $x = -\pi/4$ and so, using this value for the variable, we obtain

$$-\frac{\pi}{4} = -1 + 0 + \frac{1}{3} + 0 - \frac{1}{5} + \ldots$$

$$\frac{\pi}{4} = 1 - \frac{1}{3} + \frac{1}{5} + \ldots$$

Review problems

12 Determine the Fourier series for the function

$f(t) = x$ for $-\pi < x < \pi$, period 2π

and hence obtain the series for when $x = \pi/2$.

Further problems

13 Determine graphically the waveform generated by the following Fourier series:

$y = 2\cos \omega t + \cos 3\omega t$

14 What are the amplitude and phase of a waveform expressed as a single sinusoid if $y = 2\cos 5t - 3\sin 5t$?
15 What are the amplitude and phase of a waveform expressed as a single sinusoid if $y = 2\cos 10t + 3\sin 10t$?
16 Determine the Fourier series for the waveforms shown in figure 2.16.
17 Determine the Fourier series for the waveforms, period T, described by the following:
(a) $y = 0$ for $0 \le t < 5$, $y = 2$ for $5 \le t < 10$, $T = 10$,
(b) $y = -t$ for $-\pi \le t < 0$, $y = t$ for $0 \le t < \pi$, $T = 2\pi$,
(c) $y = A$ for $0 \le t < \pi$, $y = -A$ for $\pi \le t < 2\pi$, $T = 2\pi$,
(d) $y = t$ for $0 \le t < \pi$, $y = 0$ for $\pi \le t < 2\pi$, $T = 2\pi$,

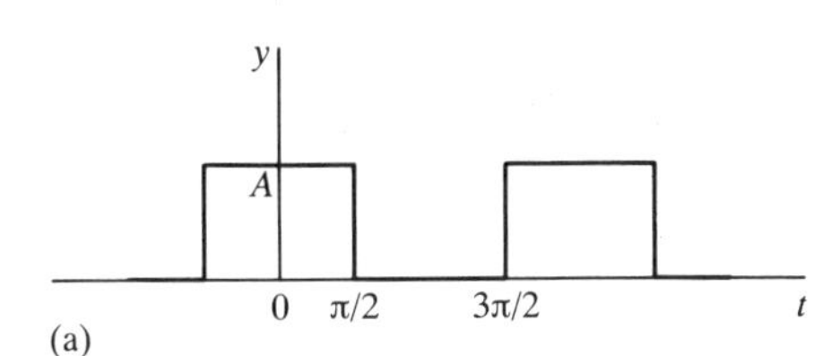

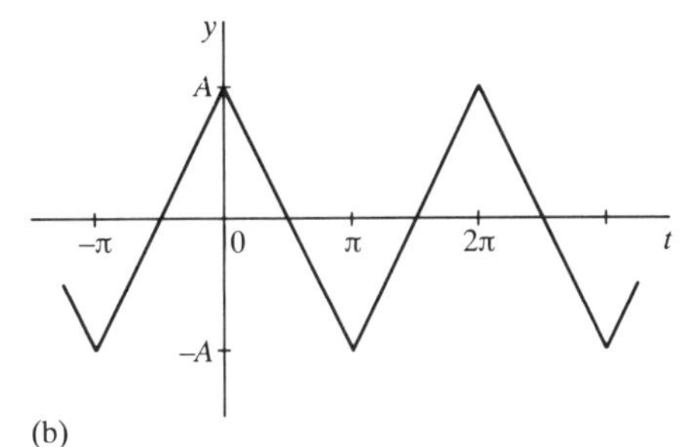

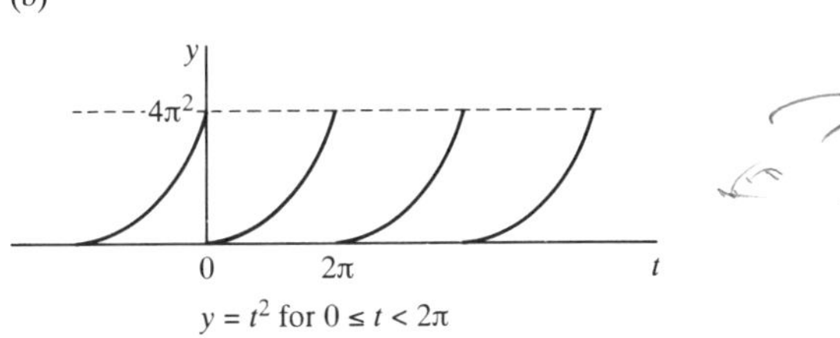

Fig. 2.16 Problem 16

(e) $y = 0$ for $-\pi \le t < 0$, $y = t$ for $0 \le t < \pi$, $T = 2\pi$,
(f) $y = 3$ for $-\pi \le t < 0$, $y = -2$ for $0 \le t < \pi$, $T = 2\pi$,
(g) $y = \pi + t$ for $-\pi \le t < 0$, $y = \pi - t$ for $0 \le t < \pi$, $T = 2\pi$,
(h) $y = t^2$ for $0 \le t < 2\pi$, $T = 2\pi$.

18 Determine the Fourier series for $f(x) = x$ for $-\pi < x < \pi$, period 2π, and show that when $x = \pi/2$

$$\frac{\pi}{4} = 1 - \frac{1}{3} + \frac{1}{5} - \frac{1}{7} + \ldots$$

19 Determine the Fourier series for $f(x) = x^2$ for $0 \le x < 2\pi$ and show that when $x = \pi$

$$\frac{\pi^2}{12} = 1 - \frac{1}{4} + \frac{1}{9} - \frac{1}{16} + \ldots$$

3 Waveform symmetry

3.1 Even and odd symmetry

The work involved in the determination of the Fourier series for a waveform can often be reduced by a consideration of its symmetry. This chapter is about the various forms of symmetry, with this section being about what is termed even and odd symmetry and the later sections about other forms of symmetry which might be encountered.

3.1.1 Even symmetry

A waveform which can be described by a value y, a function of time t, has *even symmetry* if

$$f(t) = f(-t) \qquad [1]$$

This means that the function value for a particular positive value of time is identical to that for the corresponding negative value of that time. Such a function is symmetrical about the y-axis. Figure 3.1 shows such a function. If the y-axis was a plane mirror then the reflection of the positive time values of the waveform would give the negative time values.

Figure 3.2 shows some examples of waveforms with even symmetry. Thus, for example, the cosine waveform in figure 3.2(a) has even symmetry because for all values of t we have

$$\cos t = \cos(-t)$$

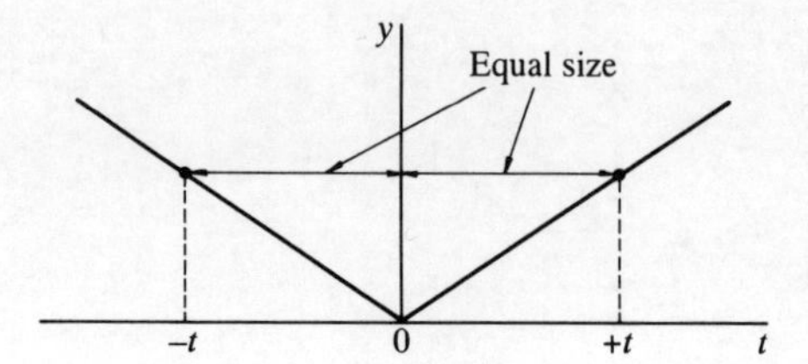

Fig. 3.1 An even function

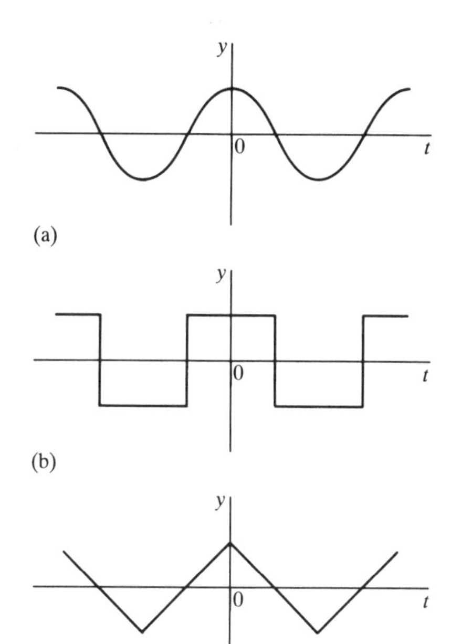

Fig. 3.2 Examples of even symmetry

3.1.2 Odd symmetry

A waveform can be described by a value y, a function of time t, as having *odd symmetry* if

$$f(t) = -f(-t) \qquad [2]$$

This means that the function value for a particular positive value of time is equal in magnitude but of opposite sign to that for the corresponding negative value of that time. Such a function is symmetrical about the origin. For every point on the waveform for positive time there is a corresponding point on the waveform on a straight line drawn through the origin and equidistant from it. Figure 3.3 shows such a function.

Figure 3.4 shows some examples of waveforms with odd symmetry. Thus, for example, the sine waveform in figure 3.4(a) has odd symmetry since

$$\sin(-t) = -\sin t$$

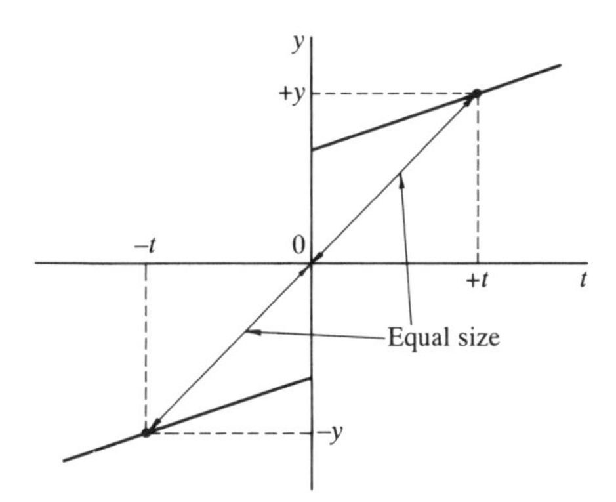

Fig. 3.3 An odd function

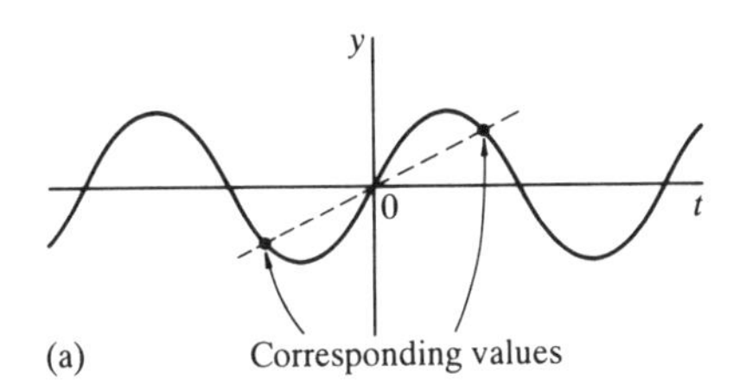

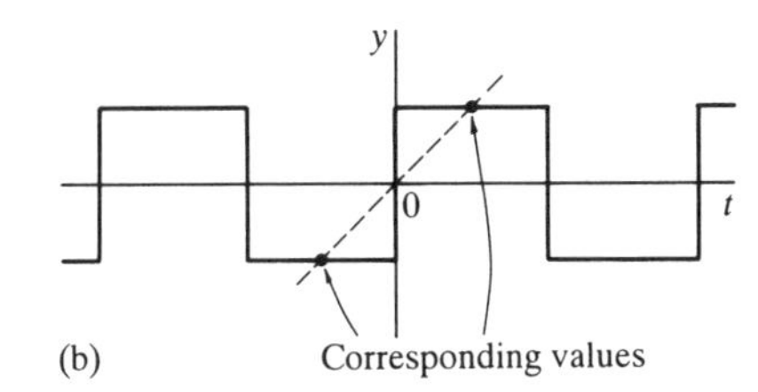

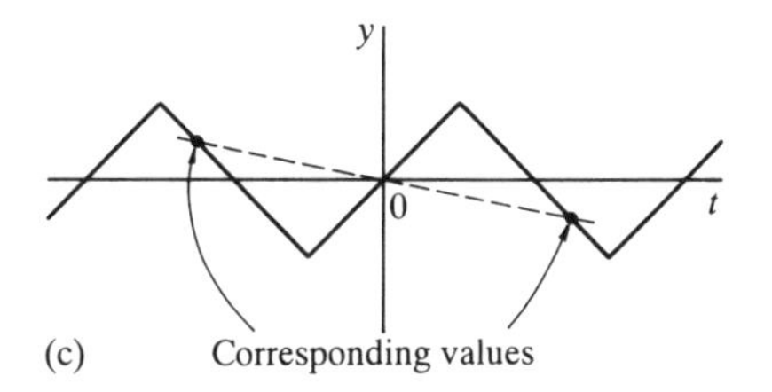

Fig. 3.4 Examples of odd symmetry

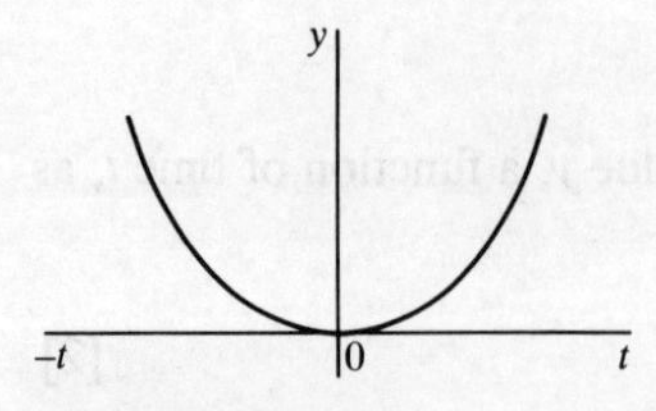

Fig. 3.5 $y = t^2$

Example

Is the waveform described by the function $y = t^2$ even or odd?

Figure 3.5 shows a graph of the waveform. The function thus describes an even function.

For an even function we must have $f(t) = f(-t)$, as in equation [1]. Thus if, for example, we take a value of t of 2 then the value of y when $t = +2$ must be the same as the value when $t = -2$. In this case we have $2^2 = (-2)^2$.

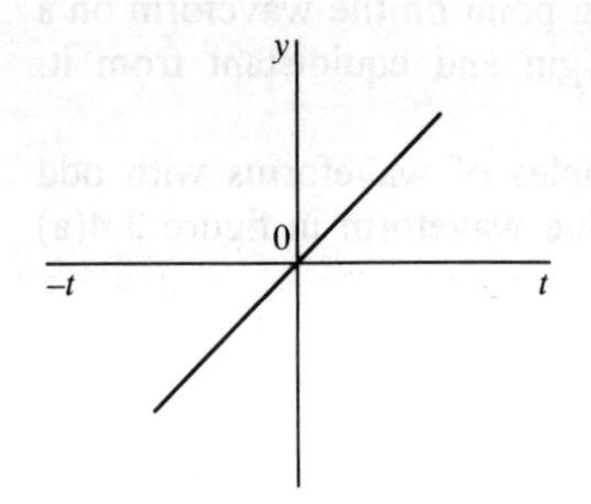

Fig. 3.6 $y = t$

Example

Is the waveform described by the function $y = t$ even or odd?

Figure 3.6 shows a graph of the waveform. The function thus describes an odd function.

For an odd function we must have $f(t) = -f(-t)$, as in equation [2]. Thus, for example, if we take a value of t of 2 then the value of y when $t = +2$ must be the same as minus the value of y when $t = -2$. In this case we have $+2 = -(-2)$.

Review problems

1 Determine the symmetry of the waveforms shown in figure 3.7.

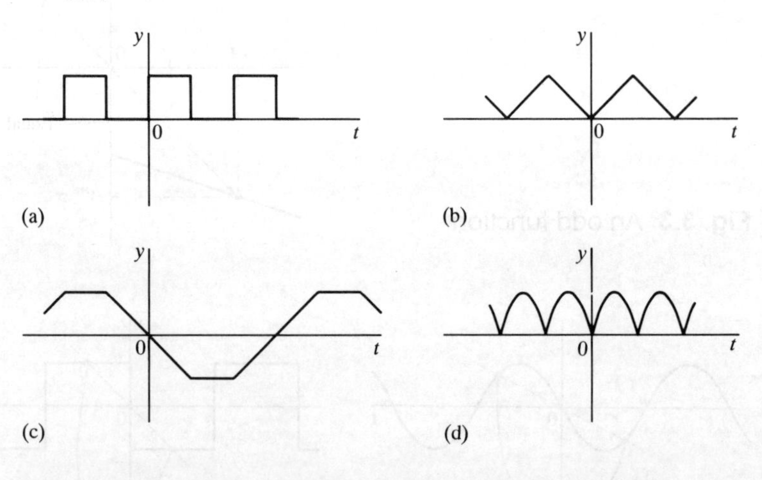

Fig. 3.7 Problem 1

2 Determine the symmetry of the waveforms described by the functions (a) $y = \cos t$, (b) $y = 5t$, (c) $y = t^3$, (d) $y = 2 + t^2$.

3.1.3 Addition of even and odd functions

The even or odd nature of the sum of two even or two odd functions can be determined using the rules:

even + even = even [3]

odd + odd = odd [4]

even + odd = indeterminate [5]

These rules can be proved as follows.

For the sum of two even functions $f(t)$ and $g(t)$ we have, for the resulting function $F(t)$,

$$F(\mathrm{t}) = f(t) + g(t)$$

Hence for a time of $-t$ we have

$$F(-t) = f(-t) + g(-t)$$

However, because $f(t)$ is even, we have $f(t) = f(-t)$ (see equation [1]). Likewise, $g(t) = g(-t)$. Thus

$$F(-t) = f(t) + g(t) = F(t)$$

This is the condition for the sum function to be even. Thus even plus even equals even.

For the sum of two odd functions $f(t)$ and $g(t)$ we have, for the resulting function $F(t)$,

$$F(t) = f(t) + g(t)$$

Hence for a time of $-t$ we have

$$F(-t) = f(-t) + g(-t)$$

However, because $f(t)$ is odd, we have $f(-t) = -f(t)$ (see equation [2]). Likewise, $g(-t) = -g(t)$. Thus

$$F(-t) = -f(t) - g(t) = -F(t)$$

This is the condition for the sum function to be odd. Thus odd plus odd equals odd.

For the sum of an even functions $f(t)$ and odd function $g(t)$ we have for the resulting function $F(t)$

$$F(t) = f(t) + g(t)$$

Hence for a time of $-t$ we have

$$F(-t) = f(-t) + g(-t)$$

However, because $f(t)$ is even, we have $f(t) = f(-t)$ (see equation [1]). Since $g(t)$ is odd we have $g(-t) = -g(t)$. Thus

$$F(-t) = f(t) - g(t)$$

This is neither even or odd. Thus adding an even and an odd function gives a function which is neither even or odd.

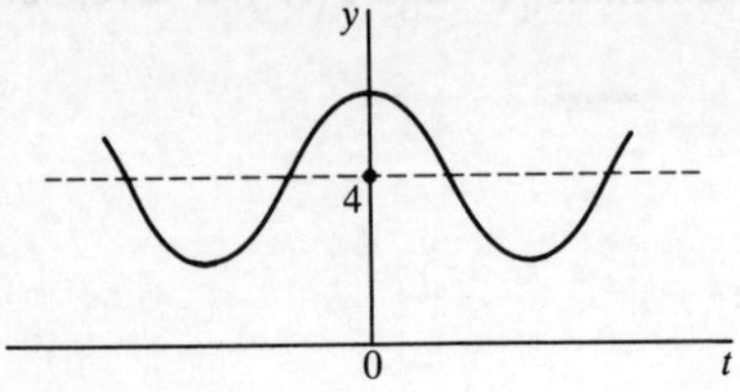

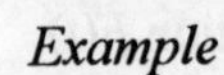

Example

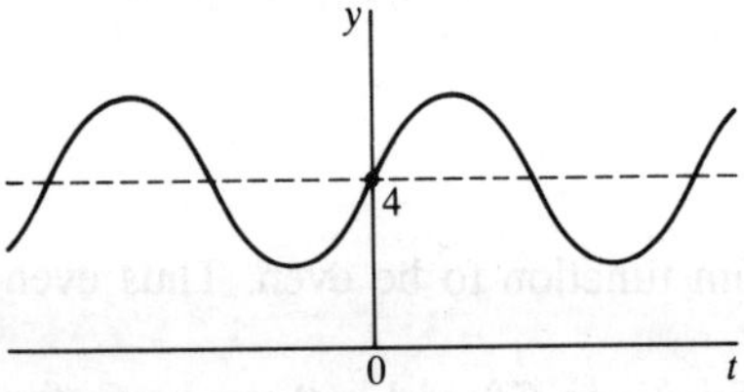

Are the functions of time described by the following even or odd? (a) $y = 4 + \cos t$, (b) $y = 4 + \sin t$.

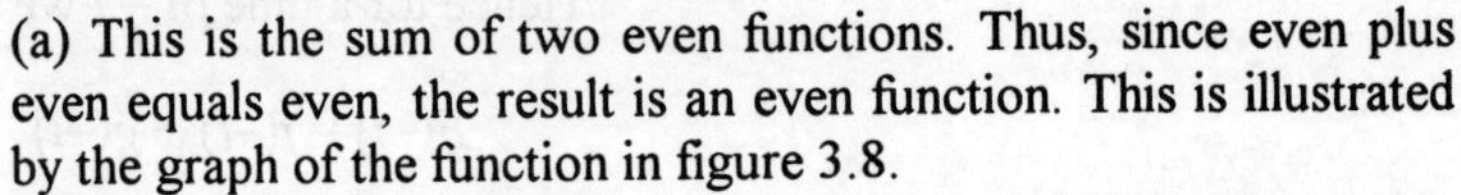

(a) This is the sum of two even functions. Thus, since even plus even equals even, the result is an even function. This is illustrated by the graph of the function in figure 3.8.

Fig. 3.8 $4 + \cos t$

(b) This is the sum of an even and an odd function. Thus, since even plus odd equals indeterminate, the result is a function which is neither even or odd. This is illustrated by the graph in figure 3.9.

Fig. 3.9 $4 + \sin t$

Review problems

3 Are the following functions even, odd or indeterminate? (a) $y = \cos 2t + \cos 3t$, (b) $y = \sin t + \sin 2t$, (c) $y = 2 + t^2$, (d) $y = 3 + t^3$, (e) $y = 5 + \sin 3t$.

3.1.4 Products of even and odd functions

The even or odd nature of the product of two even or odd functions can be determined using the rules:

$$\text{even} \times \text{even} = \text{even} \qquad [6]$$

$$\text{odd} \times \text{odd} = \text{even} \qquad [7]$$

$$\text{even} \times \text{odd} = \text{odd} \qquad [8]$$

These rules can be proved as follows.

For the product of two even functions $f(t)$ and $g(t)$ we have, for the resulting product function $F(t)$,

$$F(t) = f(t)g(t)$$

Hence, for a time of $-t$,

$$F(-t) = f(-t)g(-t)$$

However, because $f(t)$ is even, we have $f(t) = f(-t)$ (see equation [1]). Likewise, $g(t) = g(-t)$. Thus

$$F(-t) = f(t)g(t)$$

and so $F(-t) = F(t)$ and the product function is even.

For the product of two odd functions $f(t)$ and $g(t)$ we have, for the resulting product function $F(t)$,

$$F(t) = f(t)g(t)$$

Hence, for a time of $-t$,

$$F(-t) = f(-t)g(-t)$$

However, because $f(t)$ is odd, we have $f(t) = -f(-t)$ (see equation [2]). Likewise, $g(t) = -g(-t)$. Thus

$$F(-t) = [-f(t)][-g(t)] = f(t)g(t)$$

and so $F(-t) = F(t)$ and the product function is even.

For the product of an even function $f(t)$ and an odd $g(t)$ we have, for the resulting product function $F(t)$,

$$F(t) = f(t)g(t)$$

Hence, for a time of $-t$,

$$F(-t) = f(-t)g(-t)$$

However, because $f(t)$ is even, we have $f(t) = f(-t)$ (see equation [1]). Since $g(t)$ is odd we have $g(t) = -g(-t)$. Thus

$$F(-t) = [f(t)][-g(t)] = -f(t)g(t)$$

and so $-F(-t) = F(t)$ and the product function is odd.

Example

Are the following functions of time t even or odd?
(a) $y = t^2 \cos t$, (b) $y = 2t \cos 3t$.

(a) Since t^2 is an even function of time and $\cos t$ is an even function of time, we have the product of two even functions. Hence the result is an even function.
(b) Since $2t$ is an odd function of time and $\cos 3t$ is an even function of time, we have the product of an odd and an even function. Hence the result is an odd function.

Review problems

4 Are the following functions of time t even or odd?
(a) $y = t \sin t$, (b) $y = t^2 \cos^2 3t$, (c) $y = \sin 2t \sin 3t$, (d) $y = \sin 5t \cos 2t$, (e) $y = (2 + t^2) \sin 3t$.

3.2 Fourier series with even or odd symmetry

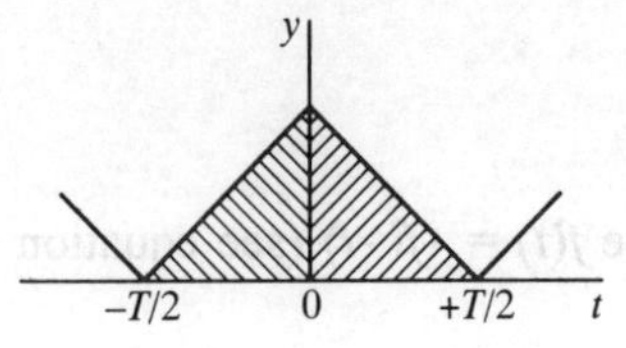

Fig. 3.10 An even function

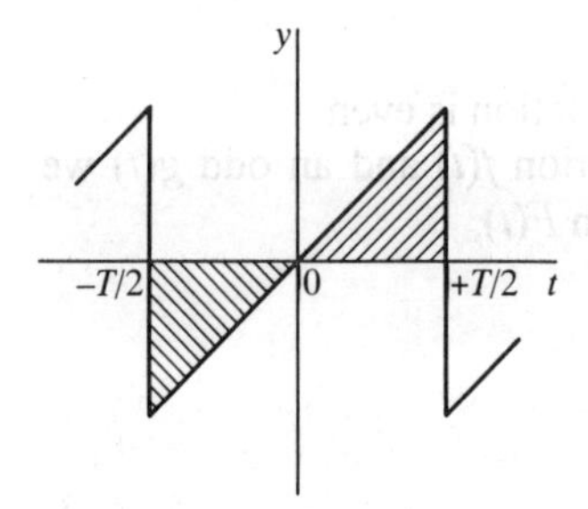

Fig. 3.11 An odd function

Consider an even function $f(t)$, as for example in figure 3.10. For such a function we have the areas on each side of the y-ordinate as being equal in both size and sign. Thus we have

$$\int_{-T/2}^{0} f(t)\,dt = \int_{0}^{T/2} f(t)\,dt$$

Thus, for the total area under the function, we can write

$$\int_{-T/2}^{T/2} f(t)\,dt = 2\int_{0}^{T/2} f(t)\,dt, \text{ when the function is even} \quad [9]$$

Consider an odd function $f(t)$, as for example in figure 3.11. For such a function we have the areas on each side of the y-ordinate as being equal in size but opposite in sign. The total area is thus zero. Hence

$$\int_{-T/2}^{T/2} f(t)\,dt = 0, \text{ when the function is odd} \quad [10]$$

Now consider the Fourier coefficients for an even function $f(t)$, using equation [18] from chapter 2,

$$a_n = \frac{2}{T}\int_{-T/2}^{T/2} f(t)\cos n\omega t\,dt$$

If $f(t)$ is even then, since $\cos n\omega t$ is even, the product $f(t) \cos n\omega t$ is even. Hence we can write, on the basis of the argument used to obtain equation [9],

$$a_n = 2 \times \frac{2}{T}\int_{0}^{T/2} f(t)\cos n\omega t\,dt \quad [11]$$

Using equation [20] from chapter 2,

$$b_n = \frac{2}{T}\int_{-T/2}^{T/2} f(t)\sin n\omega t\,dt$$

If $f(t)$ is even then, since $\sin n\omega t$ is odd, the product $f(t) \sin n\omega t$ is odd. Thus, on the basis of the discussion used to arrive at equation [10],

$$b_n = 0 \qquad [12]$$

Now consider the Fourier coefficients for an odd function $f(t)$, using equation [18] from chapter 2,

$$a_n = \frac{2}{T}\int_{-T/2}^{T/2} f(t)\cos n\omega t \,\mathrm{d}t$$

If $f(t)$ is odd then, since $\cos n\omega t$ is even, the product $f(t) \cos n\omega t$ is odd. Hence, on the basis of the discussion used to derive equation [10],

$$a_n = 0 \qquad [13]$$

Using equation [20] from chapter 2,

$$b_n = \frac{2}{T}\int_{-T/2}^{T/2} f(t)\sin n\omega t \,\mathrm{d}t$$

If $f(t)$ is odd then, since $\sin n\omega t$ is odd, the product $f(t) \sin n\omega t$ is even. Hence, on the basis of the discussion used to derive equation [9],

$$b_n = 2 \times \frac{2}{T}\int_{0}^{T/2} f(t)\sin n\omega t \,\mathrm{d}t \qquad [14]$$

Thus, to sum up. If a function $f(t)$ is defined over the interval $-T/2 < t < T/2$ then if $f(t)$ is even the Fourier series has $b_n = 0$ and so only cosine terms exist. Note that the a_0 terms is considered to be a cosine term with the cosine being $\cos n\omega t$ and $n = 0$. If $f(t)$ is odd the Fourier series has $a_n = 0$ (this also means $a_0 = 0$) and so only sine terms exist.

Example

Determine whether the waveform described by the following will have a Fourier series with only sine, only cosine or both sine and cosine terms:

$$f(t) = 2 + t^2 \text{ for } -\pi < t < \pi, \text{ period } 2\pi$$

This function is the addition of two even functions and so is even. Thus the Fourier series will contain only cosine terms.

Example

Determine the Fourier series of the waveform described by the function $y = f(t) = t$ over the interval $-\pi < t < \pi$ if the period is 2π.

The function is odd and so we have $a_n = 0$ and so only sine terms. Using equation [14],

$$b_n = 2 \times \frac{2}{T}\int_0^{T/2} f(t)\sin n\omega t \, dt$$

$$= \frac{4}{2\pi}\int_0^{\pi} t \sin n\omega t \, dt$$

Using integration by parts,

$$b_n = \frac{2}{\pi}\left[-\frac{t}{n\omega}\cos n\omega t + \frac{1}{n^2\omega^2}\sin n\omega t\right]_0^{\pi}$$

Since $\omega = 1$, then

$$b_n = \frac{2}{\pi}\left[-\frac{\pi}{n}\cos n\pi\right]$$

When n is odd then $b_n = 2/n$ and when n is even then $b_n = -2/n$. Thus the series is

$$y = 2\left(\sin t - \tfrac{1}{2}\sin 2t + \tfrac{1}{3}\sin 3t - \tfrac{1}{4}\sin 4t + \ldots\right)$$

Review problems

5 Determine the Fourier series for the following functions:
(a) $y = f(t) = t^3$ for the interval $-\pi < t < \pi$, period 2π,
(b) $y = f(t) = 2 + t^2$ for the interval $-\pi < t < \pi$, period 2π.

6 Determine whether the following functions will have only cosine, sine or both cosine and sine terms in their Fourier series:
(a) $f(t) = 2t$ for the interval $-\pi < t < \pi$, period 2π,
(b) $f(t) = t^2 \cos t$ for the interval $-\pi < t < \pi$, period 2π,
(c) $f(t) = t^3 \sin 3t$ for the interval $-\pi < t < \pi$, period 2π,
(d) $f(t) = t^4 \sin 2t$ for the interval $-\pi < t < \pi$, period 2π,
(e) $f(t) = (2 + 4t) \sin t$ for the interval $-\pi < t < \pi$, period 2π,
(f) $f(t) = t + \pi$ for the interval $-\pi < t < 0$, $f(t) = t - \pi$ for the interval $0 < t < \pi$, period $= 2\pi$.

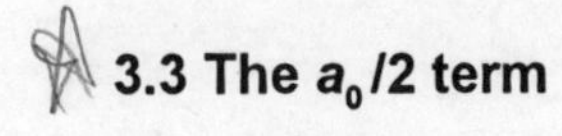

3.3 The $a_0/2$ term

Consider the waveform shown in figure 3.12. The term a_0 is given by (chapter 2 equation [16])

$$a_0 = \frac{2}{T}\int_{-T/2}^{T/2} y \, dt$$

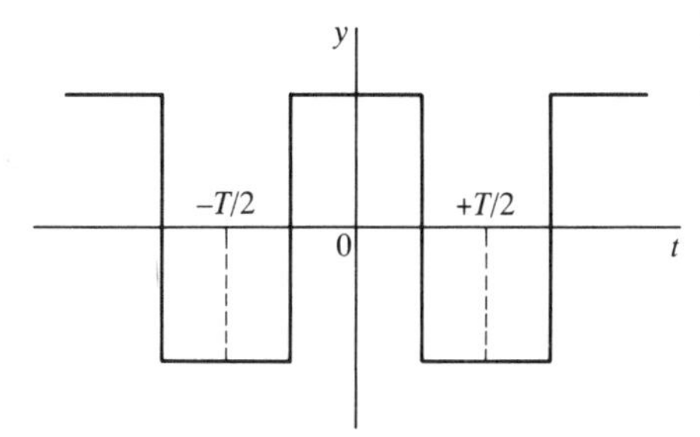

Fig. 3.12 Waveform symmetrical about time axis

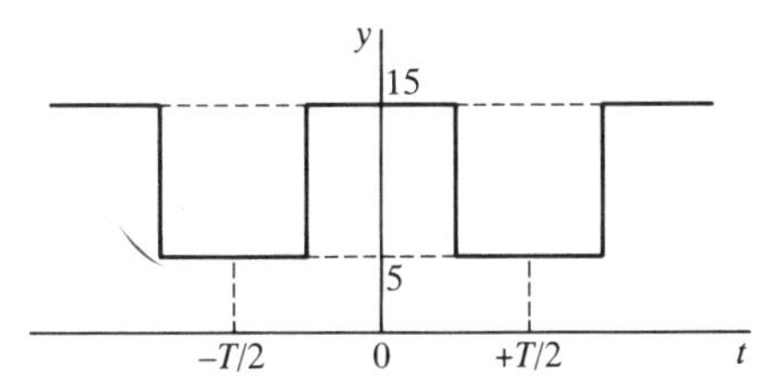

Fig. 3.13 Example

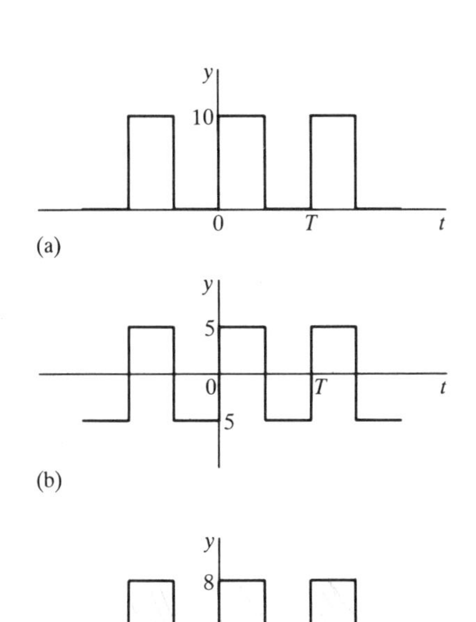

Fig. 3.14 Problem 7

However, the average value over one cycle of the waveform is given by

$$\bar{y} = \frac{\text{area under waveform}}{\text{period}}$$

$$= \frac{\int_{-T/2}^{T/2} y\,dt}{T}$$

Thus the significance of the $a_0/2$ term in the Fourier series is that it represents the average value of y over one cycle of the waveform. Thus, for the waveform in figure 3.12, because the waveform is symmetrical about the time axis the average value is zero. Thus a_0 is zero. It is only when a waveform is not symmetrical about the time axis that there is an a_0 term.

Example

What will be the value of the $a_0/2$ term for the waveform shown in figure 3.13.

This waveform has an average value over a period of 10 and so we have $a_0/2 = 10$.

Review problems

7 What will be the value of the $a_0/2$ term for the waveforms shown in figure 3.14.

3.3.1 Fourier series of sums of functions

The Fourier coefficients of the sum of two functions are the sums of the coefficients for each of the functions considered separately. This allows us to consider some waveforms as the sum of two other waveforms for which we might already know the Fourier coefficients. There are, for example, many situations where the waveform can be considered to be a standard waveform to which a d.c. signal has been added. It also enables us to carry out the operation outlined in the previous section in which a change in the time axis is considered (also see section 2.4.5 where a change of origin is considered).

Consider the waveform shown in figure 3.15(a). We can consider this waveform to be made up of two waveforms, these being shown in figures 3.15(b) and (c). Thus, for the waveform shown in figure 3.15(b) we have, using item 2 in table 2.1,

$$y = \frac{4A/2}{\pi}\left(\sin t + \frac{1}{3}\sin 3t + \frac{1}{5}\sin 5t + \dots\right)$$

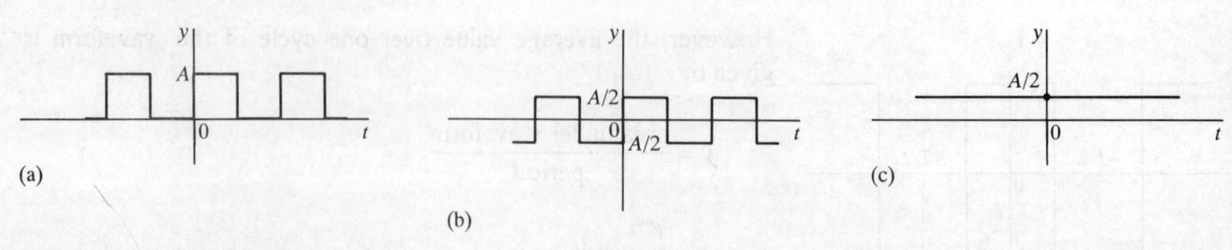

Fig. 3.15 Simplification using the sum of two functions

For the waveform in figure 3.15(c) we have

$$y = \frac{A}{2}$$

Thus the waveform in figure 3.15(a) has the Fourier series

$$y = \frac{A}{2} + \frac{2A}{\pi}\left(\sin t + \frac{1}{3}\sin 3t + \frac{1}{5}\sin 5t + \ldots\right)$$

In the above example we have, in effect, been concerned with the shifting of the time-axis by $A/2$. The result of this has added $A/2$ to the a_0 term. There are many situations where a waveform for which the Fourier coefficients are known can be transformed into the required waveform by a shift of the time-axis.

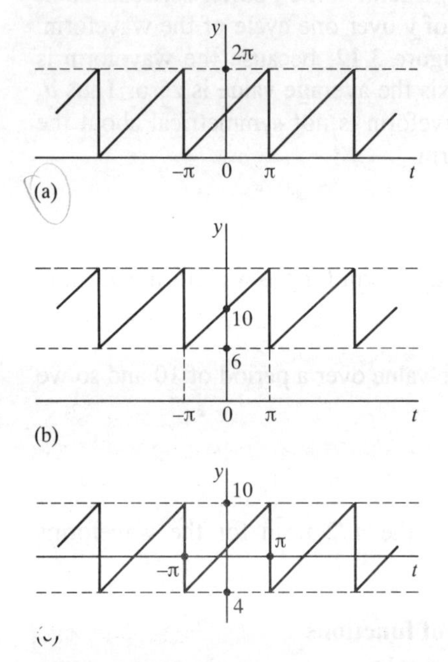

Fig. 3.16 Problem 8

Review problems

8 Determine the Fourier series for the waveforms shown in figure 3.16 by considering it to be the sum of two simpler waveforms and using waveforms for which the Fourier coefficients are given in table 2.1.

3.4 Half-wave symmetries

There are some forms of symmetry which can be identified in order to eliminate terms from the Fourier series on the basis of whether n is even or odd. The coefficient with $n = 0$ is considered to be even on this basis. These forms of symmetry are sometimes referred to as *half-wave repetition* and *half-wave inversion*.

Consider the waveform shown in figure 3.17. For such a waveform we have

$$f(t) = f(t + T/2) \qquad [15]$$

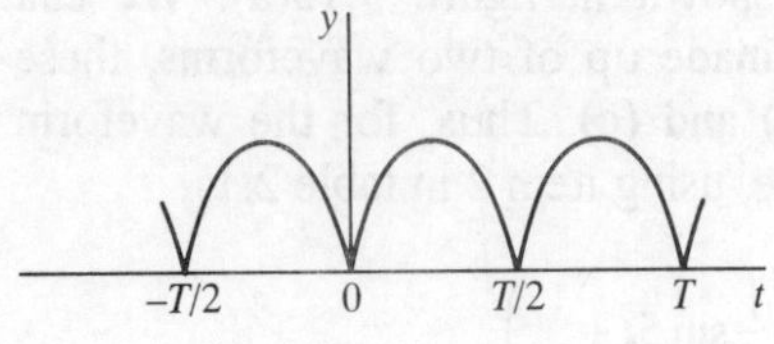

Fig. 3.17 Half-wave repetition

This is when successive halves of the waveform are identical, e.g. the first half of a waveform is identical with the second half of the

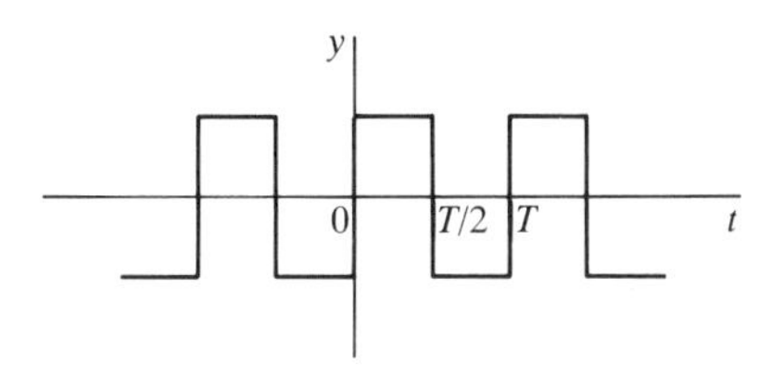

Fig. 3.18 Half-wave inversion

waveform. Such symmetry is referred to as *half-wave repetition*. With such symmetry, only terms having even values of n are present, i.e. the Fourier series has only even harmonics. See, for example, the derivation of the Fourier series for a half-wave rectified sinusoid in section 2.4.3.

Consider the waveform shown in figure 3.18. For such a waveform we have

$$-f(t) = f(t + T/2) \qquad [16]$$

This is when successive halves of a waveform are inverted forms of previous halves. Such symmetry is referred to as *half-wave inversion*. With such symmetry, only terms having odd values of n are present, i.e. the Fourier series has only odd harmonics. See, for example, the derivation of the Fourier series for a rectangular waveform given in section 2.4.1.

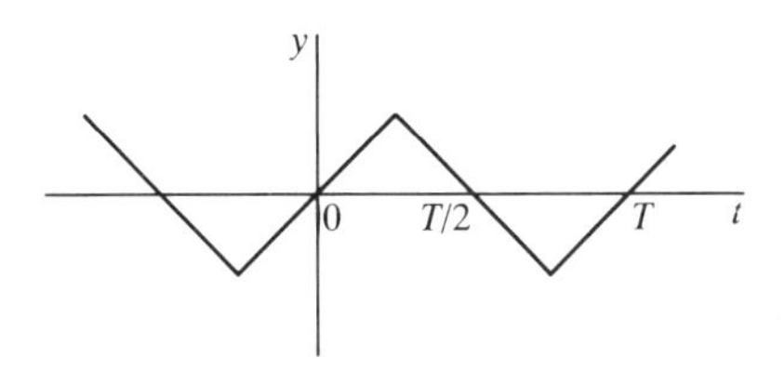

Fig. 3.19 Example

Example

On the basis of a consideration of its symmetry, determine what terms will be present in the Fourier series of the waveform shown in figure 3.19.

The waveform is odd-symmetrical and so there will only be b_n terms present. The waveform also shows half-wave inversion and so only odd values of n will be present. Thus there will only be terms in the series for b_n = 1, 3, 5, ...

Review problems

9 On the basis of a consideration of symmetry, determine what terms will be present in the Fourier series of the waveforms shown in figure 3.20.

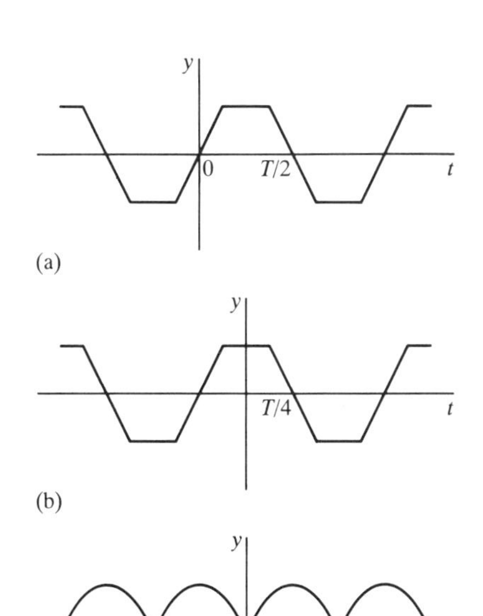

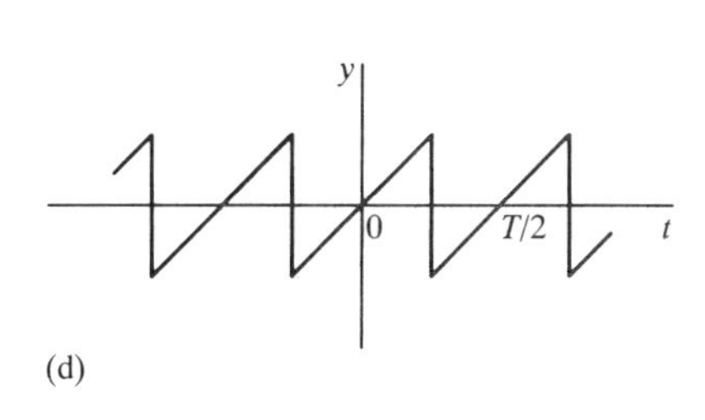

Fig. 3.20 Problem 9

Further problems

10 Determine the symmetry of the waveforms shown in figure 3.21.

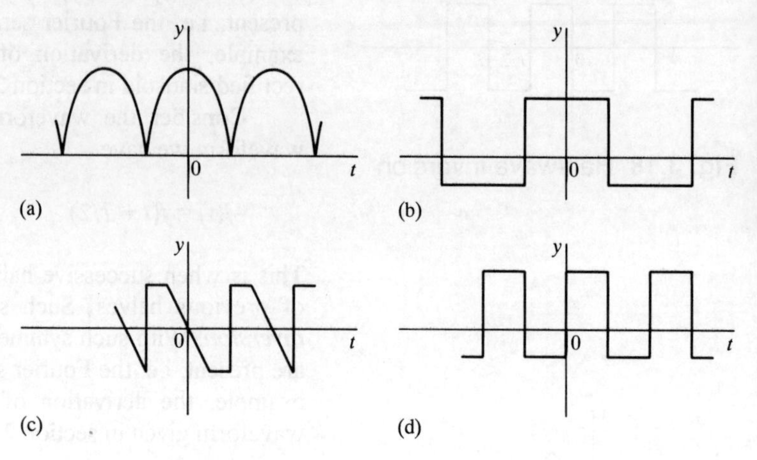

Fig. 3.21 Problem 10

11 Determine the symmetry of the waveforms described by the equations:
(a) $y = 3t^2$, (b) $y = 2 + t$, (c) $y = 2 \cos t$, (d) $y = \cos^2 t$,
(e) $y = 2$, (f) $y = 5t$, (g) $y = 2 + \cos 3t$, (h) $y = 2 + 3t$,
(i) $y = t + t^3$, (j) $y = 2t + t^2$, (k) $y = t + 3$, (l) $y = \cos t + \cos 2t$,
(m) $y = 2 \sin^2 t \cos 3t$, (n) $y = t^2 \sin t$, (o) $y = (1 + 2t^2) \sin 3t$,
(p) $y = \sin 4t \sin 5t$.

12 Determine whether the following functions will have only cosine terms, only sine terms or both:
(a) $f(t) = t$ for the interval $-\pi < t < \pi$, period 2π,
(b) $f(t) = t + t^3$ for the interval $-\pi < t < \pi$, period 2π,
(c) $f(t) = \cos 2t \cos 3t$ for the interval $-\pi < t < \pi$, period 2π,
(d) $f(t) = 4 + t$ for the interval $-\pi < t < \pi$, period 2π,
(e) $f(t) = \sin 2t \sin 3t$ for the interval $-\pi < t < \pi$, period 2π,
(f) $f(t) = 2 + 2t$ for $-1 < t < 0$, $f(t) = 0$ for $0 < t < 1$, period 2.

13 Determine the Fourier series for the following functions:
(a) $f(t) = t - \pi$ for $-\pi < t < 0$, $f(t) = t + \pi$ for $0 < t < \pi$, period 2π,
(b) $f(t) = t^2$ for $-\pi < t < \pi$, period 2π,
(c) $f(t) = 2t/\pi$ for $-\pi < t < \pi$, period 2π,
(d) $f(t) = -2$ for $-\pi < t < 0$, $f(t) = 2$ for $0 < t < \pi$, period 2π.

14 Shows that if $f(t)$ is odd then $f^2(t)$ is even.

15 Shows that if $f(t)$ is even then $f^2(t)$ is even.

16 From a consideration of symmetry, what terms will be present in the Fourier series of the waveforms shown in figure 3.22?

17 What will be the value of the $a_0/2$ terms in the Fourier series of the waveforms shown in figure 3.23?

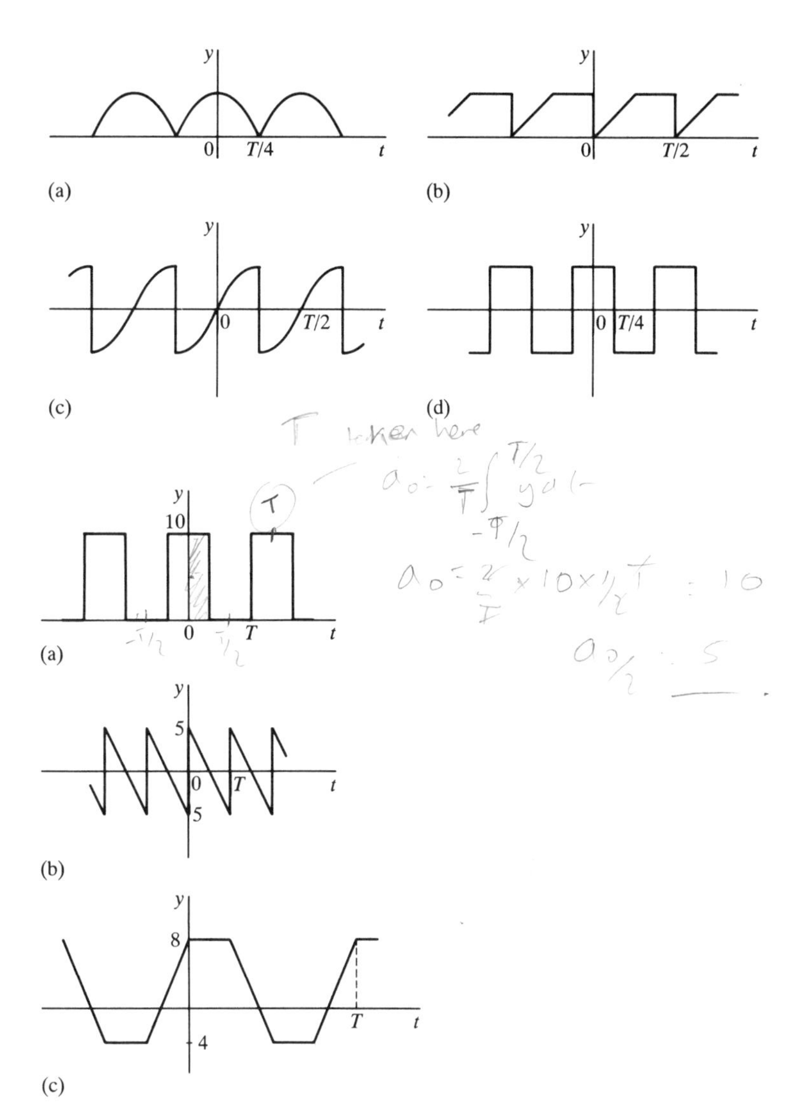

Fig. 3.22 Problem 16

Fig. 3.23 Problem 17

4 Non-periodic functions

4.1 Non-periodic functions

Sometimes in engineering we are concerned not with a periodic function, i.e. one which keeps on repeating itself every period, but one that is defined only over a finite time interval. For example, figure 4.1 shows a periodic function which can be described by

$$f(t) = t \text{ for } 0 \leq t < 5$$
$$f(t + 5) = f(t)$$

Such a function keeps on repeating itself with a period of 5. We can describe such a function by a Fourier series, as has been done in chapters 2 and 3. One of the requirements for the Fourier series to be a valid representation of a waveform is that the function being described must be continuous or piecewise continuous over time (see section 2.2.1). This means it must be a periodic function extending over all values of time.

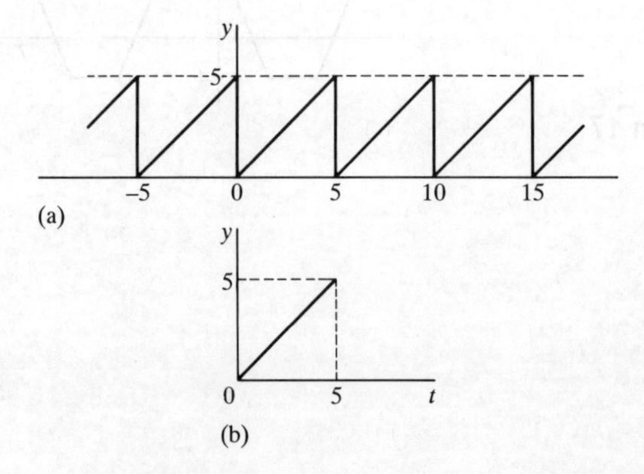

Fig. 4.1 (a) Periodic function, (b) non-periodic function

Figure 4.2 shows a non-periodic function which can be described by just

$$f(t) = t \text{ for } 0 \leq t < 5$$

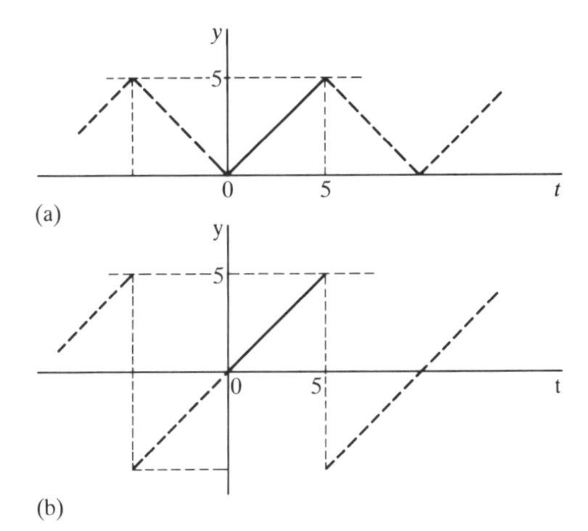

Fig. 4.2 Half-wave periodic extension

For such a function we have no knowledge, or interest in, what happens outside the time interval described by $0 \le t < 5$. Since the function is not continuous or piecewise continuous over time it would seem as if we cannot describe such a function by a Fourier series. However, since we are not interested in what the function does outside our time interval $0 \le t < 5$ we can consider it to be extended in any way we choose. Thus if we take our interval to be half a period then, for example, we might consider it extended in the way shown in figure 4.2(a) or perhaps 4.2(b). We can then write the Fourier series. Whichever extension is chosen, the resulting Fourier series only gives a representation of our function in the interval $0 \le t < 5$ and as this has been selected to be just half a period the result is termed the *half-range series*.

The function described by the waveform in figure 4.2(a) is an even function. Thus it will only contain cosine terms. The average value of the waveform is 2.5 and so $a_0/2 = 2.5$. The waveform also shows half-wave inversion and so only odd values of n are present. The waveform is described by (item 4 table 2.1)

$$y = 2.5 - \frac{20}{\pi^2}\cos\frac{\pi}{5}t - \frac{20}{9\pi^2}\cos\frac{3\pi}{5}t - \dots$$

The function described by the waveform in figure 4.2(b) is an odd function. Thus it will contain only sine terms. The waveform is described by (item 3 table 2.1)

$$y = -\frac{5}{\pi}\sin\frac{\pi}{5}t - \frac{5}{\pi}\sin\frac{2\pi}{5}t - \frac{5}{\pi}\sin\frac{3\pi}{5}t - \dots$$

Thus the half-range series for our function in figure 4.1(b) can be described by either a cosine or a sine series, depending on the way we extend the function.

So far we have discussed the extension of a non-periodic

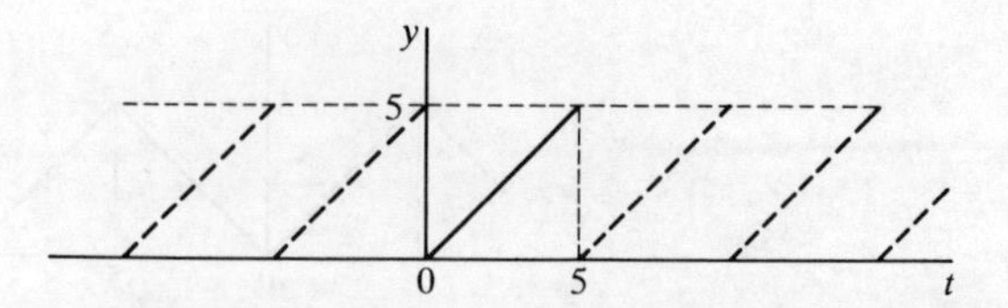

Fig. 4.3 Full range extension

function by a half-range series, i.e. we have taken the function to represent half a period. We could, however, have taken the function to represent a full-period or perhaps a quarter-period and so give a *full-range series* representation or a *quarter-range series* representation. We can, in fact, choose any length of periodic extension. Figure 4.3 shows how the non-periodic function in figure 4.1(b) can be extended if we take the function to represent a full-period. A crucial factor that determines the choice of periodic extension is the rate at which the series converges (see section 2.2.1). The more rapidly the series converges, the less the number of comp- onents needed for the series to represent the function. Another factor that may determine the choice of periodic extension is the form of the resulting series. It might, for example, be useful in some situations if the series is in the form of just sines, with no cosines or a value at $t = 0$.

4.2 Half range series

Half-range series can be written for a function in terms of just cosines or just sines (as illustrated above). For the *half-range cosine series* we have an extension which makes the function even. Then

$$a_0 = \frac{4}{T}\int_0^{T/2} f(t)\,dt \qquad [1]$$

$$a_n = \frac{4}{T}\int_0^{T/2} f(t)\cos n\omega t\,dt \qquad [2]$$

$$b_n = 0 \qquad [3]$$

and

$$y = \tfrac{1}{2}a_0 + \sum_{n=0}^{n=\infty} a_n \cos n\omega t \qquad [4]$$

For the *half-range sine series* we have an extension which makes the function odd. Then

$$a_0 = 0 \qquad [5]$$

$$a_n = 0 \qquad [6]$$

$$b_n = \frac{4}{T}\int_0^{T/2} f(t)\sin n\omega t\,\mathrm{d}t \qquad [7]$$

and

$$y = \sum_{n=0}^{n=\infty} b_n \sin n\omega t \qquad [8]$$

Example

Determine the half-range cosine series representation of the function described by

$f(t) = 2t$ for $0 \le t < 1/2$,
$f(t) = 2(1 - t)$ for $1/2 \le t < 1$

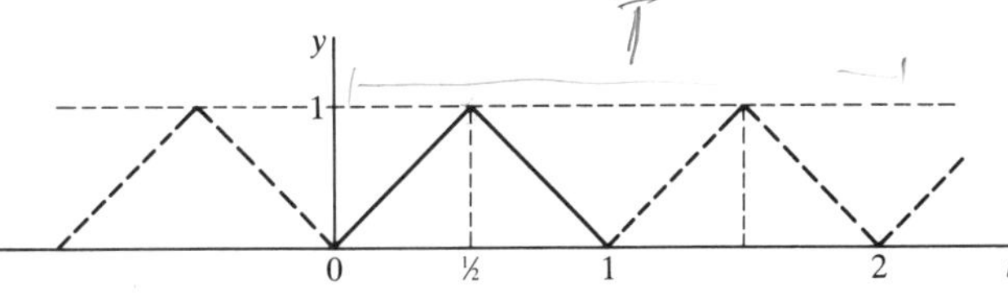

Fig. 4.4 Example

If the function is to be represented by a cosine function then it must have even symmetry. Figure 4.4 shows the function and how we might extend it to give even symmetry. Since there is half-wave repetition there will only be even values for n. The period is $T = 2$ and so $\omega = \pi$. Thus a_0 is given by equation [1] as

$$a_0 = \frac{4}{T}\int_0^{T/2} f(t)\,\mathrm{d}t$$

$$= 2\int_0^{1/2} 2t\,\mathrm{d}t + 2\int_{1/2}^{1} 2(1-t)\,\mathrm{d}t$$

$$= 1$$

Using equation [2] we have

$$a_n = \frac{4}{T}\int_0^{T/2} f(t)\cos n\omega t\,\mathrm{d}t$$

$$= 4\int_0^{1/2} 2t\cos n\pi t\,\mathrm{d}t + 4\int_{1/2}^{1} 2(1-t)\cos n\pi t\,\mathrm{d}t$$

Using integration by parts (see the Appendix),

$$\int u\,\mathrm{d}v = uv - \int v\,\mathrm{d}u$$

with, for the first integral, $u = 2t$ and $\mathrm{d}v = \cos n\pi t\,\mathrm{d}t$ and, for the second integral, $u = 2(1 - t)$ and $\mathrm{d}v = \cos n\pi t\,\mathrm{d}t$, then

$$a_n = 4\left[\frac{2t}{n\pi}\sin n\pi t + \frac{2}{n^2\pi^2}\cos n\pi t\right]_0^{1/2} + 4\left[\frac{2}{n\pi}\sin n\pi t - \frac{2t}{n\pi}\sin n\pi t - \frac{2}{n^2\pi^2}\cos n\pi t\right]_{1/2}^{1}$$

Thus

$$a_n = \frac{4}{n^2\pi^2}\left(2\cos\frac{n\pi}{2} - \cos n\pi - 1\right)$$

When n is an odd number then $a_n = 0$. When n is an even number then $a_2 = -16/2^2\pi^2$, $a_4 = 0$, $a_6 = -16/6^2\pi^2$. The half-range series is thus

$$f(t) = \frac{1}{2} - \frac{16}{2^2\pi^2}\cos 2\pi t - \frac{16}{6^2\pi^2}\cos 6\pi t - \ldots$$

Review problems

1 Determine the half-range cosine series representations of the following functions:
(a) $f(t) = 1$ defined over the interval $0 \le t < 1$,
(b) $f(t) = 2t - 1$ defined over the interval $0 \le t < 1$,
(c) $f(t) = \sin \pi t$ defined over the interval $0 \le t < 1$.

2 Determine the half-range sine series representations of the following functions:
(a) $f(t) = 1$ defined over the interval $0 \le t < 1$,
(b) $f(t) = t^2$ defined over the interval $0 \le t < 1$,
(c) $f(t) = 2 - t$ defined over the interval $0 \le t < 2$.

Further problems

3 Determine the half-range cosine and the half-range sine series representations of the following functions:
(a) $f(t) = t$ defined over the interval $0 \le t < 4$,
(b) $f(t) = \sin^2 t$ defined over the interval $0 \le t < \pi$,
(c) $f(t) = 0$ for $0 \le t < \pi/2$ and $f(t) = 1$ for $\pi/2 \le t < \pi$,
(d) $f(t) = 1 - t$ defined over the interval $0 \le t < 1$,
(e) $f(t) = \sin 3t$ defined over the interval $0 \le t < \pi$,
(f) $f(t) = \cos t/2$ defined over the interval $0 \le t < \pi$,
(g) $f(t) = \pi - t$ defined over the interval $0 \le t < \pi$,
(h) $f(t) = \pi/2$ for $0 \le t < \pi/2$ and $f(t) = 0$ for $\pi/2 \le t < \pi$.

4 A non-periodic function is described by $f(t) = \pi - t$ over the time interval $0 \le t < \pi$. Determine, by means of a suitable extension of the function, a Fourier series to represent it if the series is to have a zero value at time $t = 0$.

5 A non-periodic function is described by $f(t) = t$ over the time interval $0 \leq t < \pi$. Determine, by means of a suitable extension of the function, a Fourier series to represent it if the series is to have a finite value at time $t = 0$.

6 Determine the Fourier series which can be used to represent the displacement of a string which is fixed at both ends of a length L and pulled aside by y_0 at the distance from one end x of $L/4$. The series should have a zero value at $x = 0$.

7 Show that the function described by figure 4.5 can be described by

$$y = \frac{8}{\pi^2}\left(\sin\frac{2\pi t}{L} - \frac{1}{9}\sin\frac{6\pi t}{L} + \frac{1}{25}\sin\frac{10\pi t}{L} - \dots\right)$$

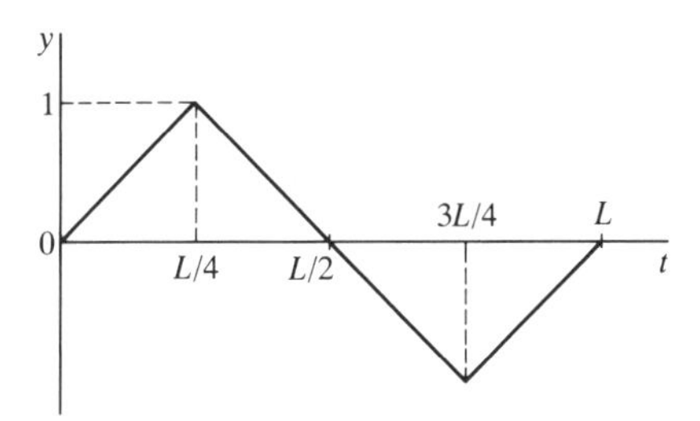

Fig. 4.5 Problem 7

5 The exponential form

5.1 Complex notation

The form used for the Fourier series in previous chapters has consisted of cosine and sine terms. There is, however, another form that can be used; one which more directly gives the amplitude terms in the frequency spectrum and relates to phasor notation. This form involves the use of complex numbers. See the Appendix for a discussion of complex numbers.

Cosines and sines can be expressed in complex notation (see the Appendix) as

$$\cos\theta = \frac{e^{j\theta} + e^{-j\theta}}{2} \quad [1]$$

$$\sin\theta = \frac{e^{j\theta} - e^{-j\theta}}{2j} \quad [2]$$

Thus the Fourier series (chapter 2 equation [8])

$$y = \tfrac{1}{2}a_0 + \sum_{n=1}^{\infty} a_n \cos n\omega t + \sum_{n=1}^{n=\infty} b_n \sin n\omega t \quad [3]$$

can be written as

$$y = \tfrac{1}{2}a_0 + \sum_{n=1}^{\infty} a_n \frac{e^{jn\omega t} + e^{-jn\omega t}}{2} + \sum_{n=1}^{n=\infty} b_n \frac{e^{jn\omega t} - e^{-jn\omega t}}{2j}$$

Multiplying the b_n term by j/j and rearranging we obtain

$$y = \tfrac{1}{2}a_0 + \sum_{n=1}^{\infty} \left(\frac{a_n - jb_n}{2} e^{jn\omega t} + \frac{a_n + jb_n}{2} e^{-jn\omega t} \right) \quad [4]$$

We can simplify this equation by replacing the Fourier coefficients a_0, a_n and b_n by complex coefficients c_0, c_n and c_{-n}.

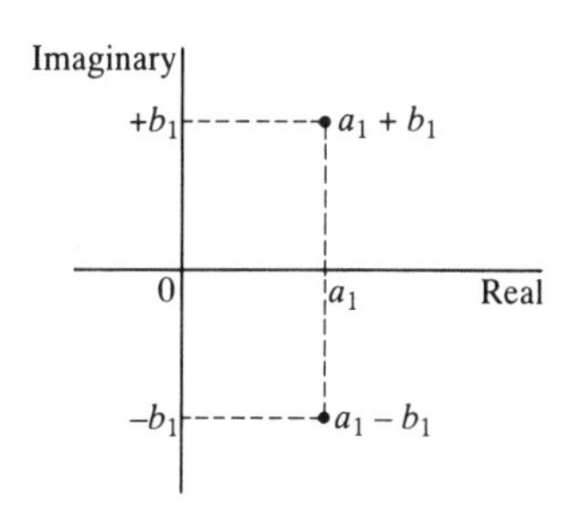

Fig. 5.1 The conjugate pair for $n = 1$

$$c_0 = \tfrac{1}{2}a_0 \qquad [5]$$

$$c_n = \frac{a_n - \mathrm{j}b_n}{2} \qquad [6]$$

$$c_{-n} = \frac{a_n + \mathrm{j}b_n}{2} \qquad [7]$$

This means that c_{-n} is the complex conjugate of c_n and is thus sometimes written as c_n^*, the * indicating a complex conjugate. Figure 5.1 shows such a pair of conjugates. Equation [4] can thus be written as

$$y = c_0 + \sum_{n=1}^{\infty} c_n \mathrm{e}^{\mathrm{j}n\omega t} + \sum_{n=1}^{n=\infty} c_{-n} \mathrm{e}^{-\mathrm{j}n\omega t}$$

Since $\mathrm{e}^0 = 1$, we can absorb the c_0 term into the summation since it is just another term to be added to the summation of the c_n term when we allow n to take the value 0. Thus

$$y = \sum_{n=0}^{\infty} c_n \mathrm{e}^{\mathrm{j}n\omega t} + \sum_{n=1}^{n=\infty} c_{-n} \mathrm{e}^{-\mathrm{j}n\omega t}$$

We can rewrite the second of the summation terms in a different form. If, instead of summing from $n = 1$ to $n = \infty$, we sum from $n = -1$ to $n = -\infty$. Since we have made n negative we must make the exponential $\mathrm{e}^{\mathrm{j}\omega t}$ and c_{-n} becomes c_n. Thus we can write

$$y = \sum_{n=0}^{\infty} c_n \mathrm{e}^{\mathrm{j}n\omega t} + \sum_{n=-1}^{n=-\infty} c_n \mathrm{e}^{\mathrm{j}n\omega t}$$

and so, since the summations extend from $-\infty$ through -1 and 0 to $+\infty$, we can write

$$y = \sum_{n=-\infty}^{\infty} c_n \mathrm{e}^{\mathrm{j}n\omega t} \qquad [8]$$

This is the complex form or exponential form of the Fourier series for the function $y = f(t)$.

5.1.1 The complex coefficients

The complex coefficient c_n was defined by equation [6] as

$$c_n = \frac{a_n - \mathrm{j}b_n}{2}$$

However, a_n and b_n are defined by (chapter 2 equations [18] and [20])

$$a_n = \frac{2}{T}\int_{-T/2}^{T/2} y \cos n\omega t \, dt$$

$$b_n = \frac{2}{T}\int_{-T/2}^{T/2} y \sin n\omega t \, dt$$

Thus

$$c_n = \frac{1}{T}\int_{-T/2}^{T/2} y \cos n\omega t \, dt - j\frac{1}{T}\int_{-T/2}^{T/2} y \sin n\omega t \, dt$$

We can replace the cosine and sine terms by their complex equivalents, using equations [1] and [2], and so obtain

$$c_n = \frac{1}{T}\int_{-T/2}^{T/2} y\left(\frac{e^{jn\omega t} + e^{-jn\omega t}}{2}\right) dt - j\frac{1}{T}\int_{-T/2}^{T/2} y\left(\frac{e^{jn\omega t} - e^{-jn\omega t}}{2j}\right) dt$$

and so

$$c_n = \frac{1}{T}\int_{-T/2}^{T/2} y e^{-jn\omega t} \, dt \qquad [9]$$

This is a simplification compared with the form of the Fourier series involving cosines and sines. With the complex form of the series there is only one coefficient and only one integration is required.

In some calculations of coefficients the following relationships can often be useful:

$$e^{j\theta} = \cos\theta + j \sin\theta$$

$$e^{-j\theta} = \cos\theta - j \sin\theta$$

Care has also to be exercised in obtaining c_0 since with n in the denominator and $n = 0$ the expressions can end up invalid. In such situations it may be simpler to evaluate c_0 using the relationship $c_0 = a_0/2$ and the integral for a_0, i.e. equation [16] in chapter 2. Thus

$$c_0 = \frac{a_0}{2} = \frac{1}{T}\int_{-T/2}^{T/2} y \, dt \qquad [10]$$

Example

Determine the complex form of the Fourier series for the waveform shown in figure 5.2.

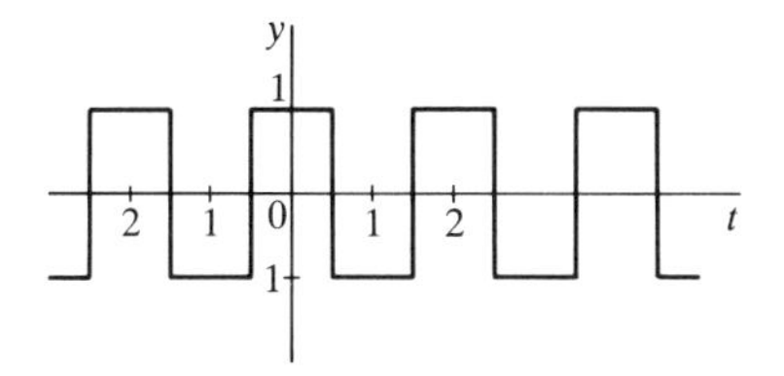

Fig. 5.2 Example

This waveform has

$$y = -1 \text{ for } -1 \leq t < -0.5$$
$$y = +1 \text{ for } -0.5 \leq t < +0.5$$
$$y = -1 \text{ for } +0.5 \leq t < +1$$

with a period of $T = 2$, and hence $\omega = \pi$. Equation [9] thus gives

$$c_n = \frac{1}{T}\int_{-T/2}^{T/2} y\mathrm{e}^{-\mathrm{j}n\omega t}\,\mathrm{d}t$$

$$= \frac{1}{2}\int_{-1}^{-0.5} -1\mathrm{e}^{-\mathrm{j}n\pi t}\,\mathrm{d}t + \frac{1}{2}\int_{-0.5}^{0.5} 1\mathrm{e}^{-\mathrm{j}n\pi t}\,\mathrm{d}t + \frac{1}{2}\int_{0.5}^{1} -1\mathrm{e}^{-\mathrm{j}n\pi t}\,\mathrm{d}t$$

$$= \frac{1}{2}\left[\frac{-1}{-\mathrm{j}n\pi}\mathrm{e}^{-\mathrm{j}n\pi t}\right]_{-1}^{-0.5} + \frac{1}{2}\left[\frac{1}{-\mathrm{j}n\omega}\mathrm{e}^{-\mathrm{j}n\pi t}\right]_{-0.5}^{0.5}$$

$$+ \frac{1}{2}\left[\frac{-1}{-\mathrm{j}n\pi}\mathrm{e}^{-\mathrm{j}n\pi t}\right]_{0.5}^{1}$$

$$= \frac{1}{\mathrm{j}2n\pi}(\mathrm{e}^{\mathrm{j}n\pi/2} - \mathrm{e}^{\mathrm{j}n\pi} - \mathrm{e}^{-\mathrm{j}n\pi/2} + \mathrm{e}^{\mathrm{j}n\pi/2} + \mathrm{e}^{-\mathrm{j}n\pi} - \mathrm{e}^{-\mathrm{j}n\pi/2})$$

$$= \frac{1}{\mathrm{j}2n\pi}(2\mathrm{e}^{\mathrm{j}n\pi/2} - 2\mathrm{e}^{-\mathrm{j}n\pi/2})$$

$$= \frac{2}{n\pi}\sin\frac{n\pi}{2}$$

Thus for n having positive values, $c_1 = 2/\pi$, $c_2 = 0$, $c_3 = -2/3\pi$, $c_4 = 0$, $c_5 = 2/5\pi$, etc. For n having negative values, remember the summation is from $n = +\infty$ to $-\infty$, then we have $c_{-1} = 2/\pi$, $c_{-2} = 0$, $c_{-3} = -2/3\pi$, $c_{-4} = 0$, $c_{-5} = 2/5\pi$, etc.

To obtain c_0 we might consider putting $n = 0$ in the above equation. However, because there is n in the denominator we would end up with an invalid relationship. Thus we obtain c_0 by using equation [10].

$$c_0 = \frac{a_0}{2} = \frac{1}{T}\int_{-T/2}^{T/2} y\,\mathrm{d}t$$

$$= \frac{1}{2}\int_{-1}^{-0.5} -1\,\mathrm{d}t + \frac{1}{2}\int_{-0.5}^{0.5} 1\,\mathrm{d}t + \frac{1}{2}\int_{0.5}^{1} -1\,\mathrm{d}t$$

$$= \tfrac{1}{2}(0.5 - 1 + 0.5 + 0.5 - 1 + 0.5) = 0$$

The Fourier series is thus

$$y = \frac{2}{\pi}e^{j\omega t} - \frac{2}{3\pi}e^{j3\omega t} + \frac{2}{5\pi}e^{j5\omega t} - \dots$$
$$+ \frac{2}{\pi}e^{-j\omega t} - \frac{2}{3\pi}e^{-j3\omega t} + \frac{2}{5\pi}e^{-j5\omega t} + \dots$$

Note that with this format for the Fourier series there are both positive and negative values of ω. This format of positive and negative frequencies and complex numbers may look odd. However, we can regard it as just a way of expressing cosine functions. If pairs of negative and positive frequencies are grouped together, e.g. $(2/\pi)\ e^{j\omega t}$ and $(2/\pi)\ e^{-j\omega t}$, we can replace them by just a single cosine term, e.g. $(1/2) \times (2/\pi) \cos \omega t$.

Review problems

1 Determine the complex Fourier series representation of the function described by figure 5.3.

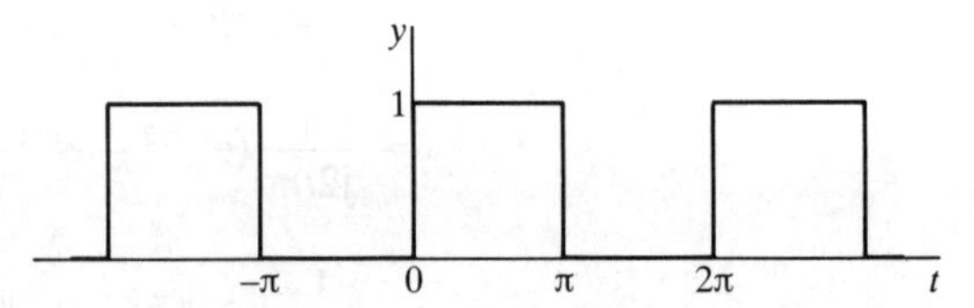

Fig. 5.3 Problem 1

5.2 Symmetry

The Fourier coefficients present in the complex form of the Fourier series are affected by the forms of symmetry present in the function $y = f(t)$. Summarising the results obtained in chapter 3:

For even symmetry $b_n = 0$ and $a_n = \frac{4}{T}\int_0^{T/2} y \cos n\omega t \, dt$

For odd symmetry $a_n = 0$ and $b_n = \frac{4}{T}\int_0^{T/2} y \sin n\omega t \, dt$

For half-wave repetition only even values of n are present

For half-wave inversion only odd values of n are present

Thus, with complex coefficients, since $c_n = (a_n - jb_n)/2$ we can write:

For even symmetry $c_n = \frac{2}{T}\int_0^{T/2} y \cos n\omega t \, dt$ [11]

For odd symmetry $c_n = -j\frac{2}{T}\int_0^{T/2} y \sin n\omega t \, dt$ [12]

For half-wave repetition only even values of n are present

For half-wave inversion only odd values of n are present

Example

What symmetries are present in the waveform described by figure 5.2 and from such a consideration determine the complex coefficients.

The waveform has even symmetry and half-wave inversion. Thus we can use equation [11] to determine c_n and there will only be odd values of n. $T = 2$ and $\omega = \pi$.

$$c_n = \frac{2}{T}\int_0^{T/2} y \cos n\omega t \, dt$$

$$= \int_0^{1/2} 1 \cos n\pi t \, dt + \int_{1/2}^{1} -1 \cos n\pi t \, dt$$

$$= \left[\frac{1}{n\pi}\sin n\pi t\right]_0^{1/2} + \left[-\frac{1}{n\pi}\sin n\pi t\right]_{1/2}^{1}$$

$$= \frac{2}{n\pi}\sin\frac{n\pi}{2}$$

Thus, as in the previous example, we have for n having positive values $c_1 = 2/\pi$, $c_2 = 0$, $c_3 = -2/3\pi$, $c_4 = 0$, $c_5 = 2/5\pi$, etc. and for n with negative values $c_{-1} = 2/\pi$, $c_{-2} = 0$, $c_{-3} = -2/3\pi$, $c_{-4} = 0$, $c_{-5} = 2/5\pi$, etc. c_0 is determined as in the previous example.

Review problems

2 Determine the complex Fourier series representation for the waveforms described by:
(a) $f(t) = 1$ for $0 \le t < 1$ and $f(t) = 0$ for $1 \le t < 2$, period = 2,
(b) $f(t) = \sin \pi t$ for $0 \le t < 1$ and $f(t) = -\sin \pi t$ for $1 \le t < 2$, period = 2 (i.e. the fully rectified sine wave).

5.3 The frequency spectrum

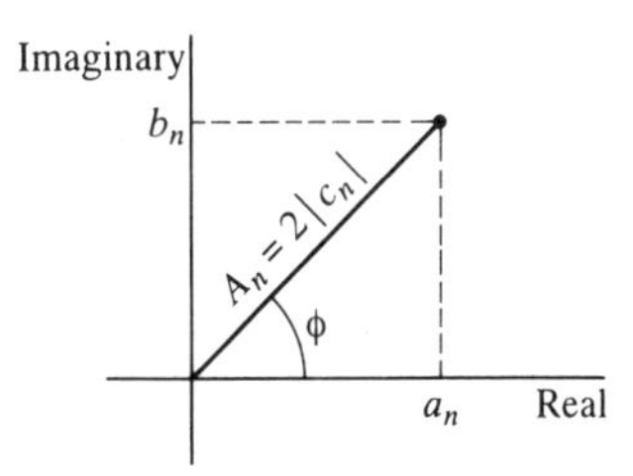

Fig. 5.4 Amplitude relationships

With the cosine and sine form of the Fourier series, the amplitude A_n of an harmonic is given by (chapter 2 equation [13])

$$A_n = \sqrt{(a_n^2 + b_n^2)}$$

This, and the definition of the phase angle ϕ, can be illustrated by figure 5.4. The amplitude A_n is the hypotenuse of a right-angled triangle for which a_n and b_n are the sides. With the complex form we can write equation [6] as

$$c_n^2 = \left(\frac{a_n - \mathrm{j}b_n}{2}\right)^2 = \frac{a_n^2 + b_n^2}{4}$$

and so

$$A_n = 2|c_n| \qquad [13]$$

Using equation [7] we can also obtain

$$A_n = 2|c_{-n}| \qquad [14]$$

Thus the complex coefficient has a magnitude which is just half that of the amplitude (see figure 5.4). We can also write

$$A_n = |c_n| + |c_{-n}| \qquad [15]$$

Thereby, by doubling the magnitudes of the coefficients to give the amplitudes, the complex coefficients more directly indicate the amplitudes of the constituent frequencies.

The complex coefficients also give information about the phase since $c_n = (a_n - \mathrm{j}b_n)/2$ and the phase is given by (chapter 2 equation [10])

$$\phi = \tan^{-1}\left(\frac{-b_n}{a_n}\right)$$

Thus if, for example, we had $c_1 = 4 - \mathrm{j}3$ then the phase would be $\tan^{-1}(3/4) = 36.8°$. Since the amplitude is $\sqrt{4^2 + 3^2} = 5$ then we have for this component an amplitude of 5 and a phase angle of 36.8°.

Example

A sawtooth waveform gives a Fourier series with complex coefficients given by

$$c_n = \mathrm{j}\frac{2}{n\pi} \text{ for } n \text{ values from } \infty \text{ to } -\infty\text{, excluding 0}$$

$$c_0 = 2$$

What will be the amplitudes and phases of the constituent waves?

The amplitude of the d.c. component will be 2 × 2; at 1ω and −1ω the amplitude is 2 × 2/π; at 2ω and −2ω it is 2 × 1/π; at 3ω and −3ω it is 2 × 2/3π, etc. Since c_0 has only a real term then the phase of that component is $\tan^{-1}(-0/2) = 0°$. Since c_1 has only an imaginary term then the phase of that component is $\tan^{-1}(-2/\pi)/0$ and so is $-90°$. This is the same for all values of c_n.

Review problems

3 A fully rectified sinusoidal waveform gives a Fourier series with complex coefficients of

$$c_n = -\frac{2}{(4n^2 - 1)\pi} \text{ for all values of } n.$$

What will be the amplitudes and phases of the constituent waves?

4 A waveform has a component in its complex Fourier series of $c_n = 2 - j4$, what will be its amplitude and phase?

5 A harmonic in a Fourier series description of a waveform is given by $4\cos\omega t - 5\sin\omega t$. What is the complex representation of this harmonic?

5.3.1 Frequency spectrum of pulses

A particular frequency spectrum which is of interest is that of a sequence of periodic pulses. This is of particular relevance in chapter 9 in the discussion of the Fourier transform.

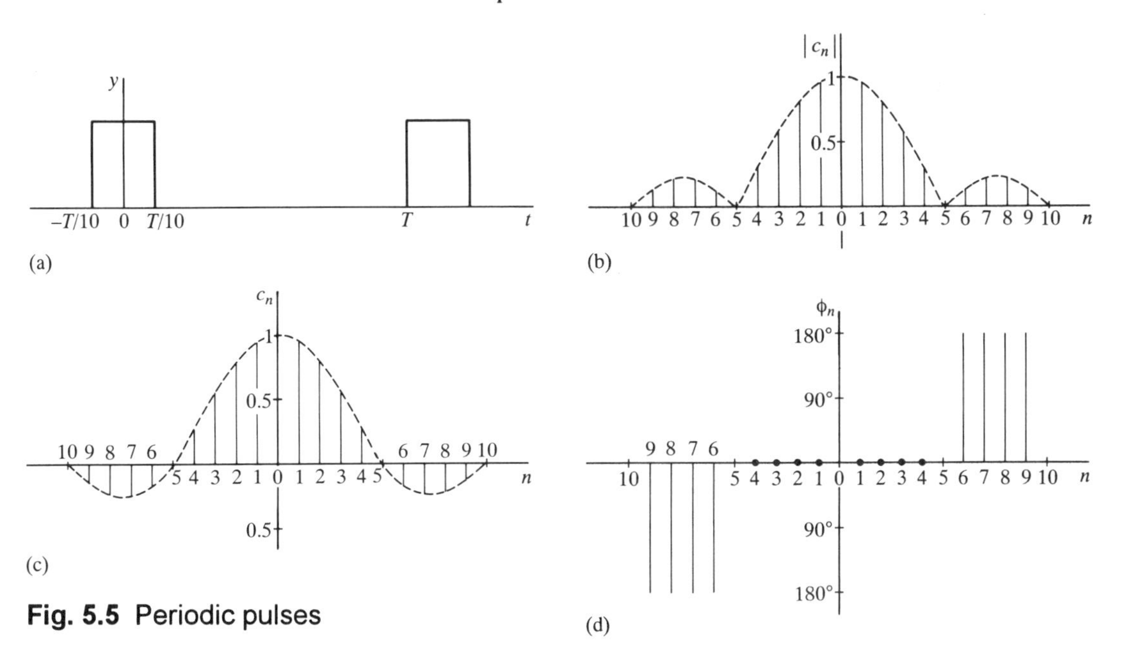

Fig. 5.5 Periodic pulses

Consider the sequence of pulses indicated in figure 5.5(a), a pulse of height 5 and width $T/5$ being repeated at a period of T. The complex coefficient is given by equation [9] as

$$c_n = \frac{1}{T}\int_{-T/10}^{T/10} 5e^{-jn\omega t}\,dt$$

$$= \frac{5}{T}\left[\frac{e^{-jn\omega t}}{-jn\omega}\right]_{-T/10}^{T/10}$$

Since $\omega = 2\pi/T$ then

$$c_n = -\frac{5}{j2n\pi}(e^{-jn\pi/5} - e^{jn\pi/5})$$

$$= \frac{5}{n\pi}\sin\frac{n\pi}{5} \qquad [16]$$

c_0 can be obtained by the use of equation [10] as

$$c_0 = \frac{1}{T}\int_{-T/10}^{T/10} 5\,dt = \frac{1}{T}[5t]_{-T/10}^{T/10} = 1$$

Equation [16] can thus be written as

$$c_n = 1\,\frac{\sin(n\pi/5)}{n\pi/5} \qquad [17]$$

and thus indicate the factor by which the amplitude of the signal is changed as the number of the harmonic is increased. Figure 5.5(b) shows a graph of how $|c_n|$ varies with n, i.e. the number of the harmonics and figure 5.5(c) the corresponding graph of c_n with n. The fifth, tenth, fifteenth, etc. harmonics are all zero. Figure 5.5(d) shows the corresponding phase angle graph. Since c_n is real with no imaginary component then we must have $\phi = \tan^{-1} \pm 0$ and so the phase angle must be 0° or ±180°, depending on the sign of the sine. When c_n is positive then $\phi = 0°$, as between $n = -4$ and $n = +4$. When c_n is negative then $\phi = \pm 180°$. Between $n = +6$ and $n = +9$ we take ϕ to be +180°, between $n = -6$ and $n = -9$ we take ϕ to be −180°.

5.4 Phasors

A sinusoidal voltage, current or other form of oscillation can be expressed in the form (see section 1.2)

$$v = V_m \sin(\omega t + \phi)$$

or

$$v = V_m \cos(\omega t + \phi)$$

where V_m is the maximum value or amplitude of the voltage, v the value at a time t and ϕ its phase angle. Euler's formula, however, gives

$$e^{j\theta} = \cos\theta + j\sin\theta$$

and so

$$e^{j(\omega t+\phi)} = \cos(\omega t+\phi) + j\sin(\omega t+\phi)$$

Multiplying throughout by V_m gives

$$V_m e^{j(\omega t+\phi)} = V_m\cos(\omega t+\phi) + jV_m\sin(\omega t+\phi)$$

Thus we can consider a sinusoidally varying voltage to be either the real or the imaginary part of $V_m e^{j(\omega t+\phi)}$, depending on whether we are considering the cosine or sine function. So we can write, for the cosine function,

$$v = \mathrm{Re}\, V_m e^{j(\omega t+\phi)}$$

Re is used to indicate that we are considering the real part of that which follows the symbol. The equation can be rewritten as

$$v = \mathrm{Re}\, V_m e^{j\omega t} e^{\phi}$$

We can consider the $e^{j\omega t}$ term to arise from the fact that a radius is rotating with an angular velocity ω (see section 1.2). ϕ is the angle, relative to some reference axis, at which the radius starts to rotate at time $t = 0$ (see section 1.2.1). The $V_m e^{j\omega t}\, e^{j\phi}$ is said to define a quantity called a *phasor*, i.e. the rotating radius which gives as its projection on the real, or imaginary, axis the sinusoidal voltage. Often, because for a particular circuit the angular frequency ω is the same for all elements, the phasor can be adequately described by just specifying its magnitude and phase angle, i.e. as $V_m\angle\phi$.

There is another way we can arrive at the relationship for a phasor. If, for example, we consider the waveform

$$v = V_m\cos(\omega t+\phi)$$

then we can write this, using $\cos\theta = (e^{j\theta} + e^{-j\theta})/2$, as

$$v = \frac{V_m}{2}\left(e^{j(\omega t+\phi)} + e^{-j(\omega t+\phi)}\right)$$

$$= \tfrac{1}{2}V_m e^{j\omega t}\, e^{j\phi} + \tfrac{1}{2}V_m e^{-j\omega t}\, e^{-j\phi}$$

Thus v can be considered to be the sum of two phasors, each with

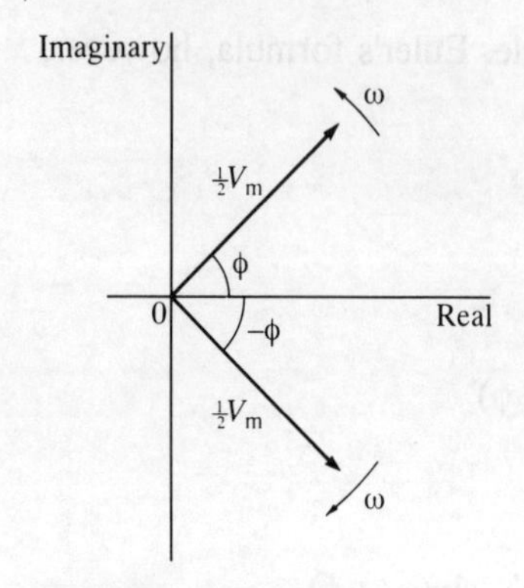

Fig. 5.6 Phasors

half the amplitude with one having a positive value of angular velocity and a positive value of ϕ and the other with a negative value of the angular velocity ω, i.e. the phasor is rotating in a clockwise direction, and a negative value of ϕ. The two phasors are $\frac{1}{2}V_m\angle\phi$ and $\frac{1}{2}V_m\angle(-\phi)$. Figure 5.6 shows the two phasors. This does not involve us considering whether it is the real or the imaginary projection of the phasor that we are interested in.

With the Fourier representation of a waveform in complex notation we have the $c_n e^{jn\omega t}$ and $c_n e^{-jn\omega t}$ terms with c_n being half the amplitude. We can thus consider that these terms represent phasors with those with positive exponentials being ones rotating with a positive angular velocity, i.e. in an anticlockwise direction, and those with negative exponentials being ones rotating with a negative angular velocity, i.e. in a clockwise direction. With $n = 0$ we have a non-rotating component since we have e^0. With $n = 1$ we have a radius rotating with an angular velocity 1ω, with $n = 2$ a radius rotating with angular velocity 2ω, with $n = 3$ a radius rotating with an angular velocity 3ω, etc. We thus have a set of phasors, the algebraic sum of which at some instant of time gives the magnitude of the waveform at that time.

Figure 5.7 illustrates this for a few terms with a rectangular waveform. Figure 5.7(a) shows the waveform. Figure 5.7(b) shows the d.c. components and the phasors due to the first, third and fifth harmonics at a time $t = 0$. The resultant of the phasors due to all the harmonics is zero. Thus at $t = 0$ we have a value for the function of $A/2$, i.e. just that due to the d.c. component. At time $t = 0$ we have a discontinuity with the function having the value 0 to one side of it and A on the other. The Fourier series thus predicts the average of these two values (see section 2.2.1). At time $t = T/8$ the phasors have rotated to the positions shown in figure 5.7(c). Now the resultant of the harmonics is $A/2$ in the same direction as the d.c. component. Thus the function has a value of 1. At time $t = 5T/8$ the phasors are as shown in figure 5.7(d). Now the resultant of the phasors due to all the harmonics is $A/2$ in the opposite direction to the d.c. component. Thus the value of the function is 0.

Example

Determine the pair of phasors that can be used to represent the voltages (a) $v = 10 \cos 3t$, (b) $v = 10 \cos (3t - \pi/2)$.

(a) Using $\cos \theta = (e^{j\theta} + e^{-j\theta})/2$ then we have

$$v = 5e^{j3t} + 5e^{-j3t}$$

Thus we have a phasor of length 5 rotating anticlockwise with an angular velocity of 3 rad/s and another phasor with length 5

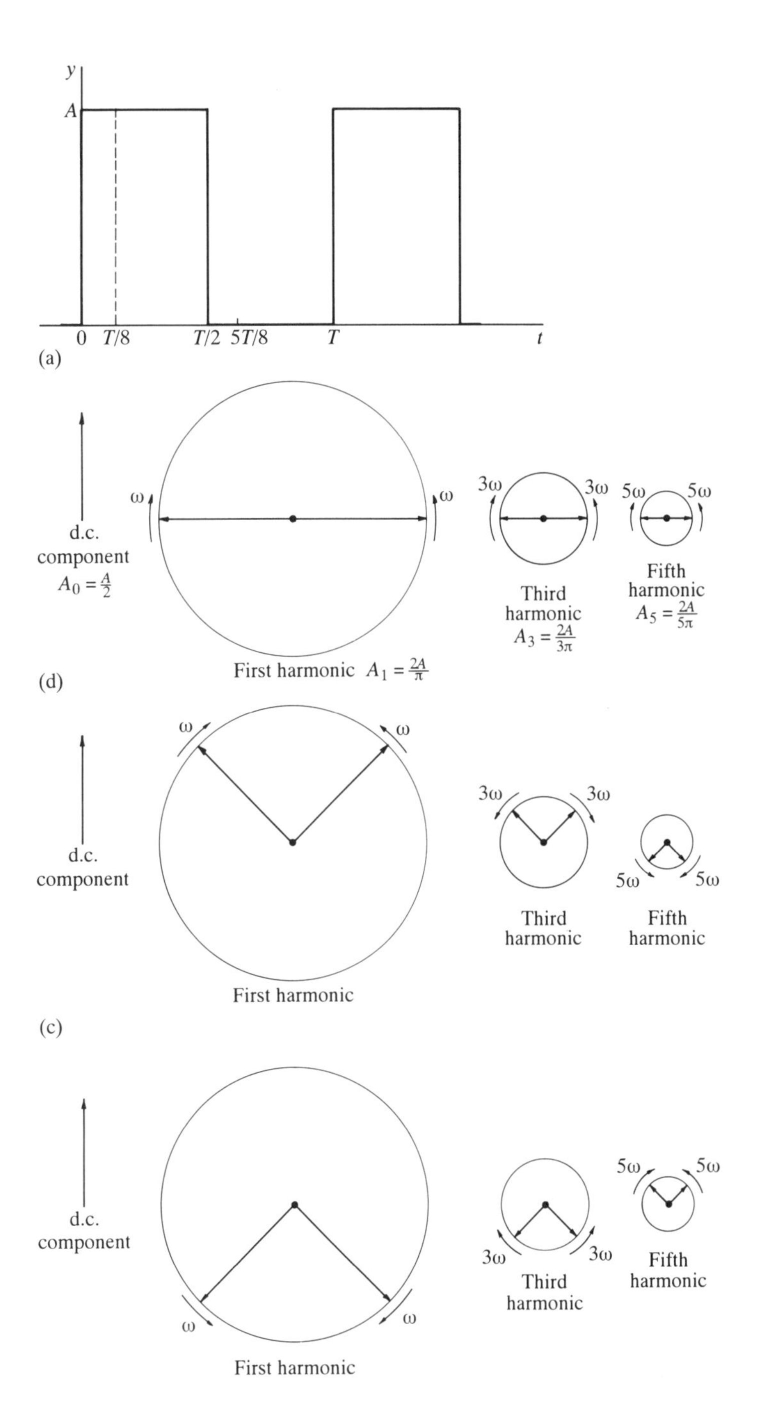

Fig. 5.7 (a) The waveform, (b) phasors at $t = 0$, (c) phasors at $t = T/8$, (d) phasors at $t = 5T/8$

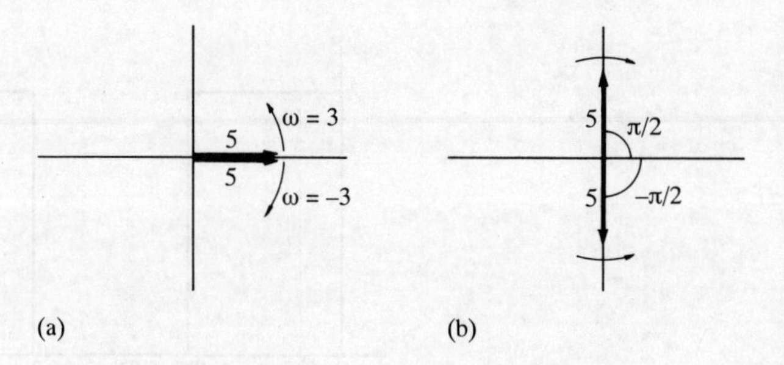

Fig. 5.8 Example

rotating clockwise with an angular velocity of 3 rad/s. Both phasors have zero phase angle. Figure 5.8(a) shows the phasors.
(b) Using $\cos\theta = (e^{j\theta} + e^{-j\theta})/2$

$$v = 5e^{j(3t-\pi/2)} + 5e^{-j(3t-\pi/2)}$$

This can be written as

$$v = 5e^{j3t}e^{-\pi/2} + 5e^{-j3t}e^{\pi/2}$$

Thus we have a phasor of length and phase angle $-\pi/2$ rotating anticlockwise with an angular velocity of 3 rad/s. We also have another phasor with length 5 and phase angle $\pi/2$ rotating clockwise with an angular velocity of 3 rad/s. Figure 5.8(b) shows the phasors.

Example

Determine the pair of phasors that can be used to represent the second harmonic in a Fourier series if it is represented by

$$y = 4\cos t - 4\pi\sin t$$

Using $\cos\theta = (e^{j\theta} + e^{-j\theta})/2$ and $\sin\theta = (e^{j\theta} - e^{-j\theta})/2j$ then

$$y = 2(e^{jt} + e^{-jt}) - \frac{2\pi}{j}(e^{jt} - e^{-jt})$$

$$= 2(e^{jt} + e^{-jt}) - \frac{j2\pi}{j^2}(e^{jt} - e^{-jt})$$

$$= (2 + j2\pi)e^{jt} + (2 - j2\pi)e^{-jt}$$

We thus have a phasor represented by $2 + j2\pi$, or $6.6\angle\pi$, which is rotating anticlockwise with an angular velocity of 1 rad/s and one represented by $2 - j2\pi$, or $6.6\angle(-\pi)$, rotating clockwise with an angular velocity of 1 rad/s.

Review problems

6 Determine the pairs of phasors that can be used to represent the voltages (a) $v = 6 \cos 4t$, (b) $v = 6 \cos (4t + \pi/2)$.

7 Determine the pair of phasors that can be used to represent the harmonic $4 \cos 2\omega t - 5 \sin 2\omega t$.

Further problems

8 Determine the complex form of the Fourier series for the waveforms described by:
(a) $f(t) = \frac{1}{4}t$ for $0 \le t < 8$, period $T = 8$,
(b) $f(t) = 1 - t$ for $0 \le t < 6$, period $T = 6$,
(c) $f(t) = 2 - 2t$ for $0 \le t < 1$, $f(t) = 0$ for $1 \le t < 2$, $f(t) = 2t - 4$ for $2 \le t < 3$, period $T = 3$,

9 A waveform gives a Fourier series with complex coefficients of

$$c_n = -\mathrm{j}\frac{3}{n\pi} \text{ for all values of } n \text{ except } n = 0,$$

$$c_0 = -\tfrac{1}{2}$$

What are the amplitudes and phases of the constituent waves?

10 A waveform gives a Fourier series with complex coefficients of

$$c_n = \mathrm{j}\frac{16}{n\pi} \text{ for all values of } n \text{ except } n = 0,$$

$$c_0 = 4$$

What are the amplitudes and phases of the constituent waves?

11 A waveform is described by the Fourier series

$$y = 10 + 8 \cos \omega t + 4 \cos 2\omega t + \dots + 6 \sin \omega t - 5 \sin \omega t + \dots$$

Derive the complex form of this series.

12 A triangular waveform is described by the Fourier series

$$y = 0.5 + 0.405 \cos \pi t + 0.045 \cos 3\pi t + 0.016 \cos 5\pi t + \dots$$

Derive the complex form of this series.

13 Determine the pairs of phasors which can be used to represent $v = 2 \cos (2t + \pi/6)$.

14 For a waveform which can be described by the following complex form of the Fourier series, plot the amplitude and phase spectrum for harmonics up to the eighth.

$$f(t) = \sum_{n=-\infty}^{\infty} \frac{2}{n\pi} \mathrm{e}^{-\mathrm{j}n\omega t}$$

6 Electric circuits

6.1 Circuit analysis

This chapter is a consideration of circuit analysis when the current or voltage waveforms applied to a circuit are perhaps square waves or half-rectified sinusoids or some other non-sinusoidal waveform. A non-sinusoidal waveform may arise from a sinusoidal waveform being applied to a component which has a non-linear characteristic. Such devices include diodes, transistors, and iron-cored inductors. The discussion in this chapter is restricted to steady-state conditions when all transients have died away.

In general, we can represent the waveforms of square waves, half-rectified sinusoids, distorted sinsusoids, etc. by a Fourier series. The basic principle used in circuit analysis with such waveforms is *superposition* in that it is assumed that we can consider each component of the Fourier series as a separate source and that the overall effect is due to the summation of the effects arising from each such source. This is a consequence of the fact that each term in a Fourier series can be differentiated or integrated term-by-term (see chapter 8). Hence we can consider the current or voltage due to each harmonic independently.

Consider the application to a circuit of a voltage which can be represented by, say,

$$v = V_0 + V_1 \sin \omega t + V_2 \sin 2\omega t + ... + V_n \sin n\omega t \qquad [1]$$

We can think of the circuit as being supplied by a number of independent sources, as illustrated in figure 6.1. Each of the sources represents one of the terms in the Fourier series. We can find the current in the circuit independently due to each of these sources and then the circuit current is the superposed value of all these currents. Thus if, for example, V_0 gave rise to a current I_0, the first harmonic $V_1 \sin \omega t$ to a current of $I_1 \sin \omega t$, the second harmonic $V_2 \sin 2\omega t$ to a current of $I_2 \sin 2\omega t$, etc., then the total current i would be

$$I_0 + I_1 \sin \omega t + I_2 \sin 2\omega t + ...$$

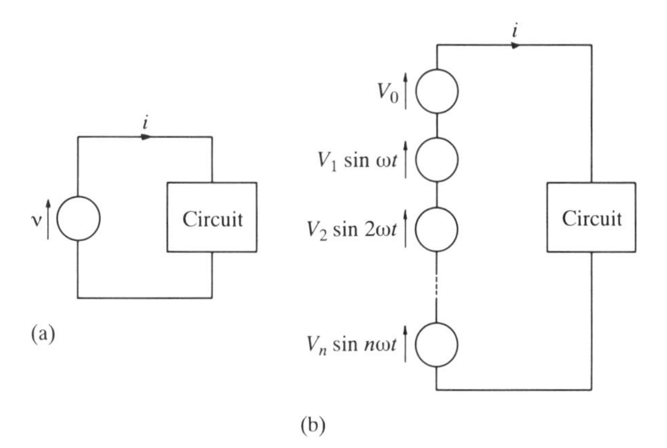

Fig. 6.1 (a) A circuit with the voltage input, (b) the equivalent circuit

6.1.1 Circuit elements

To illustrate the approach required for circuit analysis, consider the application of a non-sinusoidal voltage to individual circuit elements with pure resistance, pure inductance and pure capacitance. In the next section circuits containing combinations of such elements will be analysed. Consider the applied voltage to be

$$v = V_0 + V_1 \sin \omega t + V_2 \sin 2\omega t + \ldots + V_n \sin n\omega t$$

With a pure *resistance* the current due to the d.c. term will be V_0 /R, since we will assume Ohm's law to be valid and the current to be proportional to the voltage. The current due to the first harmonic will be $(V_1/R)\sin \omega t$. The current due to the second harmonic will be $(V_2/R)\sin 2\omega t$. Whichever harmonic is considered the resistance can be considered to be the same. Thus the circuit current resulting from all the harmonics is

$$i = \frac{V_0}{R} + \frac{V_1}{R}\sin \omega t + \frac{V_2}{R}\sin 2\omega t + .. + \frac{V_n}{R}\sin n\omega t \qquad [2]$$

Comparing this with equation [1], the current and voltage waveforms are identical in shape, since they are made up of the same sinusoidal waveforms with the amplitudes of each harmonic just scaled by the same factor $1/R$. The frequencies and phases of each harmonic are unchanged.

With a pure *inductance* the current due to a harmonic is given by

$$i = \frac{1}{L}\int v \, dt$$

Thus, for the d.c. term V_0, the current will be zero since the voltage with pure inductance is zero. For the first harmonic the current will be

$$i_1 = \frac{1}{L}\int V_1 \sin\omega t \, dt = -\frac{V_1}{\omega L}\cos\omega t$$

For the second harmonic it will be

$$i_2 = \frac{1}{L}\int V_2 \sin 2\omega t \, dt = -\frac{V_2}{2\omega L}\cos 2\omega t$$

and so on. Hence the circuit current is

$$i = 0 - \frac{V_1}{\omega L}\cos\omega t - \frac{V_2}{2\omega L}\cos 2\omega t - \ldots - \frac{V_n}{n\omega L}\cos n\omega t$$

This can be written as

$$i = \frac{V_1}{\omega L}\sin(\omega t - 90°) + \frac{V_2}{2\omega L}\sin(2\omega t - 90°)$$

$$+ \ldots + \frac{V_n}{n\omega L}\sin(n\omega t - 90°) \qquad [3]$$

For greater consistency of units, since ωt is in radians we ought to put all the terms in the brackets in radians and so write it as $(n\omega t - \pi/2)$.

The reactance for the n harmonic, i.e. V_n/I with I being the maximum value of the current for the harmonic, will depend on the frequency of that harmonic and be given by $X_{Ln} = n\omega L$. Thus for an inductance, the current waveform is of a different shape to the voltage waveform, the amplitudes of the harmonics being scaled by different factors. The current of each harmonic lags the voltage of that harmonic by 90°. Conversely we can say that the voltage leads the current by 90°. Impedance is defined as the voltage phasor divided by the current phasor, i.e. $Z = \mathbf{V}/\mathbf{I}$ (in this book, bold letters are used for phasors). Thus the impedance of the n harmonic Z_n is

$$Z_n = \frac{\mathbf{V}_n}{\mathbf{I}_n} = \frac{V_n\angle 90°}{I_n\angle 0°} = X_{Ln}\angle 90°$$

In complex notation this can be written as jX_{Ln}.

With a pure *capacitance* the current due to the voltage of a harmonic across the element is given by $i = C\,dv/dt$. Thus, for the d.c. element the current will be zero since it is not changing with time. For the first harmonic

$$i_1 = C\frac{d}{dt}(V_1 \sin\omega t) = \omega C V_1 \cos\omega t$$

For the second harmonic it is

$$i_2 = C\frac{\mathrm{d}}{\mathrm{d}t}(V_2 \sin 2\omega t) = 2\omega C V_2 \cos 2\omega t$$

Thus the circuit current is

$$i = 0 + \omega C V_1 \cos \omega t + 2\omega C V_2 \cos 2\omega t + \ldots + n\omega C V_n \cos n\omega t$$

This can be written as

$$i = \frac{V_1}{1/\omega C} \sin(\omega t + 90°) + \frac{V_2}{1/2\omega C} \sin(2\omega t + 90°)$$

$$+ \ldots + \frac{V_n}{1/n\omega C} \sin(n\omega t + 90°) \qquad [4]$$

For consistency of units the bracketed terms should be written entirely in radian measure as $(n\omega t + \pi/2)$.

The current waveform is thus of a different shape to the voltage waveform, the amplitudes of the harmonics being scaled by different factors. The reactance of the n harmonic is thus $X_{Cn} = 1/n\omega C$. The current at each harmonic leads the voltage by 90° or conversely we can say that the voltage lags the current by 90°. The impedance of the n harmonic is thus

$$Z_n = \frac{V_n \angle(-90°)}{I_n \angle 0°} = X_{Cn} \angle(-90°)$$

This can be written as $-\mathrm{j}X_{Cn}$.

Example

A 2 μF capacitor is connected across a half-wave rectified voltage supply which has an output given by

$$v = 0.32 + 0.5 \cos 100t + 0.21 \cos 200t \text{ V}$$

Determine the waveform of the current.

Using $i = C\,\mathrm{d}v/\mathrm{d}t$ then there will be no current arising from the d.c. component of 0.32 V. For the first harmonic there will be a current of

$$i_1 = 2 \times 10^{-6}(-0.5 \times 100 \sin 100t) \text{ A}$$

and for the second harmonic

$$i_2 = 2 \times 10^{-6}(-0.21 \times 200 \sin 200t) \text{ A}$$

Thus the current waveform will be

$$i = -0.1 \cos (\omega t + 90°) - 0.084 \cos (\omega t + 90°) \text{ mA}$$

or

$$i = -0.1 \cos (\omega t + \pi/2) - 0.084 \cos (\omega t + \pi/2) \text{ mA}$$

Review problems

1 A current of

$$i = 200 \sin 500t + 100 \sin 1000t \text{ mA}$$

flows through a resistance of 200 Ω. Determine the voltage waveform.

2 A voltage of

$$v = 2.5 + 3.2 \sin 100t + 1.6 \sin 200t \text{ V}$$

is applied across a 10 μF capacitor. Determine the current waveform.

3 A voltage waveform with a fundamental frequency of 1000 rad/s is applied across a capacitor of 2 μF. The waveform has first, second and third harmonics. What will be the reactances at each harmonic?

6.1.2 Series circuits

For components in series the total impedance is the sum of the impedances of the separate elements. Consider a circuit involving an inductance L in series with a resistance R when there is a voltage input to it involving harmonics and we are required to determine the current waveform. We can consider each harmonic, and any d.c. component, independently. The impedance Z_n at the n harmonic is thus given by

$$Z_n = R + \mathrm{j}X_{Ln} = R + \mathrm{j}n\omega L$$

Thus, if we had a resistance of 10 Ω and an inductance of 0.01 H with a first harmonic voltage of $50 \sin 1000t$ V, in polar notation $50\angle 0°$ V, then

$$Z_1 = 10 + \mathrm{j}(1 \times 1000 \times 0.01) = 10 + \mathrm{j}10\,\Omega$$

In polar notation this is $14.1\angle 45°\,\Omega$. The current due to the first harmonic is thus

$$i_1 = \frac{\mathbf{V}_1}{Z_1} = \frac{50\angle 0^\circ}{14.1\angle 45^\circ} = 3.5\angle(-45^\circ)\ \text{A or } 3.5\angle(-\pi/4)\ \text{A}$$

In a similar way the currents due to each of the other harmonics can be determined and so the superposition of all the currents used to obtain the circuit current.

Example

A voltage of

$$v = 2 \sin 500t + 1 \sin 1000t\ \text{V}$$

is applied to a circuit consisting of a resistance of 6 Ω in series with a capacitor which has a capacitive reactance of 8 Ω at the fundamental angular frequency of 500 rad/s. What will be the equation of the current waveform?

For the first harmonic the impedance will be

$$Z_1 = R - jX_{C1} = 6 - j8 = 10\angle(-53.1^\circ)\ \Omega$$

Thus the phasor for the first harmonic current will be

$$\mathbf{I}_1 = \frac{\mathbf{V}_1}{Z_1} = \frac{2\angle 0^\circ}{10\angle(-53.1^\circ)} = 0.2\angle 53.1^\circ\ \text{A}$$

For the second harmonic the angular frequency is twice that at the first harmonic and so the reactance must be halved to 4 Ω. Hence

$$Z_2 = R - jX_{C2} = 6 - j4 = 7.2\angle(-33.7^\circ)\ \Omega$$

Thus the phasor for the second harmonic current will be

$$\mathbf{I}_2 = \frac{\mathbf{V}_2}{Z_2} = \frac{1\angle 0^\circ}{7.2\angle(-33.7^\circ)} = 0.14\angle 33.7^\circ\ \text{A}$$

Hence the current is

$$i = 0.2 \sin (500t + 53.1^\circ) + 0.14 \sin (500t + 33.7^\circ)\ \text{A}$$

Review problems

4 Determine the current waveform through a load of resistance 10 Ω when an inductance of 0.01 H is connected in series with it and the circuit is supplied with the half-rectified voltage of 100 V peak amplitude V_m and angular frequency 1000 rad/s. The following is the Fourier series for a half-rectified

waveform when only the d.c. element and the first harmonic are considered.

$$v = \frac{V_m}{\pi}\left(1 + \frac{\pi}{2}\sin \omega t - \frac{2}{3}\cos 2\omega t\right)$$

5 Determine the amplitudes of the voltage components occurring across a load of resistance 10 Ω when an inductance of 0.01 H is connected in series with it and the circuit is supplied with the full-wave rectified voltage of 100 V peak amplitude V_m and angular frequency 1000 rad/s. The following is the Fourier series for the full-wave rectified waveform when the d.c. element and the first and second harmonics are considered.

$$v = \frac{2V_m}{\pi}\left(1 - \frac{2}{3}\cos 2\omega t - \frac{2}{15}\cos 4\omega t\right)$$

6 The rectangular waveform shown in figure 6.2 is applied to a circuit consisting of a resistance R in series with a capacitance C. Determine how the voltage across the capacitor will vary with time.

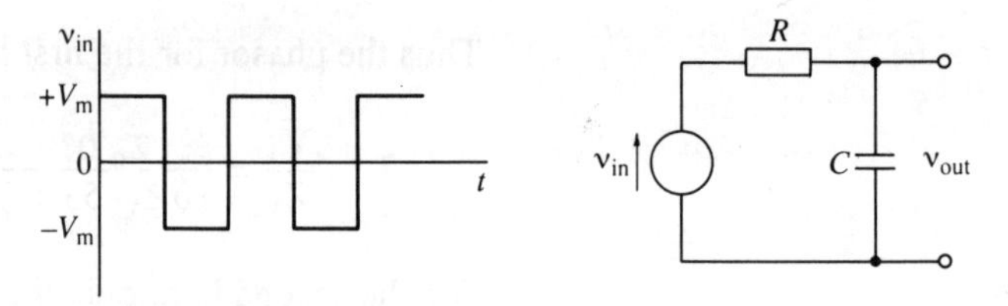

Fig. 6.2 Problem 6

6.1.3 Parallel circuits

For parallel circuits the total impedance Z_n at the n harmonic is given by

$$\frac{1}{Z_n} = \frac{1}{Z_{n1}} + \frac{1}{Z_{n2}} \quad [5]$$

where Z_{n1} and Z_{n2} are the impedances of the parallel elements for the n harmonic.

Example

Determine the circuit current waveform for a circuit consisting of a resistance of 5 Ω in parallel with an inductor having inductive reactance of 5 Ω at the angular frequency of 500 rad/s when a voltage of

$$v = 10 \sin 500t + 5 \sin 1500t \text{ V}$$

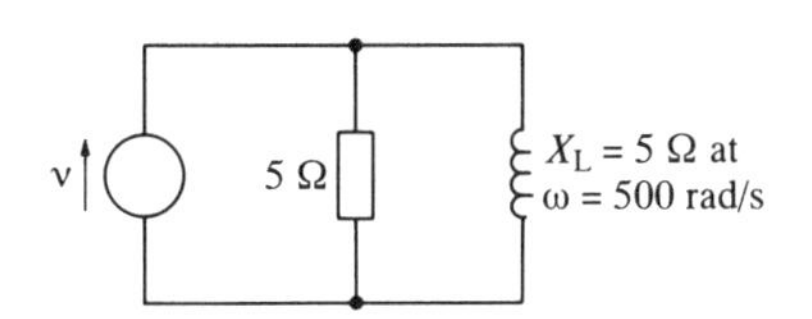

Fig. 6.3 Example

is applied.

Figure 6.3 shows the circuit. The total impedance for the first harmonic is

$$\frac{1}{Z_1} = \frac{1}{5} + \frac{1}{\text{j}5} = \frac{5 + \text{j}5}{\text{j}25}$$

$$Z_1 = \frac{\text{j}5}{1 + \text{j}1} = \frac{\text{j}5(1 - \text{j}1)}{(1 + \text{j}1)(1 - \text{j}1)} = 2.5 + \text{j}2.5 = 3.5\angle 45^\circ\ \Omega$$

The current phasor for the first harmonic is thus

$$\mathbf{I}_1 = \frac{\mathbf{V}_1}{Z_1} = \frac{10\angle 0^\circ}{3.5\angle 45^\circ} = 2.9\angle(-45^\circ)\ \text{A}$$

The reactance for the third harmonic is three times that of the first harmonic and so is 15 Ω. Thus the total impedance for the third harmonic is

$$\frac{1}{Z_3} = \frac{1}{5} + \frac{1}{\text{j}15} = \frac{5 + \text{j}15}{\text{j}75}$$

$$Z_3 = \frac{\text{j}15}{1 + \text{j}3} = \frac{\text{j}15(1 - \text{j}3)}{(1 + \text{j}3)(1 - \text{j}3)} = 4.5 + \text{j}1.5 = 4.7\angle 18.4^\circ\ \Omega$$

Hence the current phasor for the third harmonic is

$$\mathbf{I}_3 = \frac{\mathbf{V}_3}{Z_3} = \frac{5\angle 0^\circ}{4.7\angle 18.4^\circ} = 1.1\angle(-18.4^\circ)\ \text{A}$$

Thus the current waveform is

$$i = 2.9 \sin(500t - 45^\circ) + 1.1 \sin(1500t - 18.4^\circ)\ \text{A}$$

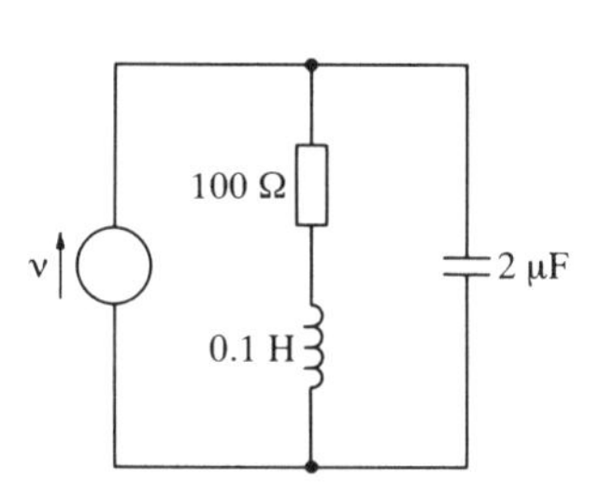

Fig. 6.4 Problem 7

Review problems

7 Determine the waveform of the current taken from the voltage source for the circuit shown in figure 6.4 when the voltage supplied has a waveform of

$$v = 10 \sin 1000t + 4 \sin 2000t + 2 \sin 3000t\ \text{V}$$

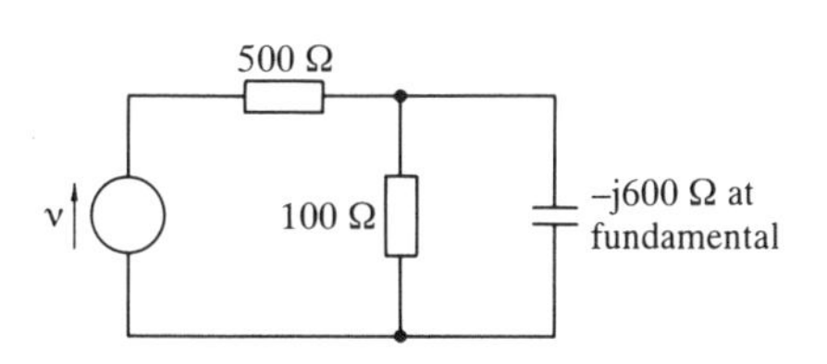

Fig. 6.5 Problem 8

8 Determine the waveform of the current taken from the voltage source for the circuit shown in figure 6.5 when the voltage supplied has a waveform of

$$v = 10 \sin 500t + 5 \sin(1500t + 30^\circ)\ \text{V}$$

6.2 Root-mean-square values

When a d.c. current I passes through a resistance R then the power dissipated is I^2R. When an alternating current i passes through a resistance then the power dissipated varies with time, being i^2R. The mean power over a time T is thus the mean value of i^2R over that time, i.e.

$$\text{mean power} = \frac{1}{T}\int_0^T i^2 R\,\mathrm{d}t$$

The equivalent d.c. current which would give this value of power is called the *root-mean-square* (r.m.s.) current. Thus the root-mean-square value of an alternating current is given by

$$I_{\text{rms}}^2 = \frac{1}{T}\int_0^T i^2\,\mathrm{d}t \qquad [6]$$

Consider the current with a waveform given by a Fourier series in the form

$$i = \frac{a_0}{2} + \sum_{n=1}^{\infty}(a_n \cos n\omega t + b_n \sin n\omega t)$$

where $\omega = 2\pi/T$. We can obtain an expression for i^2 by multiplying both sides of the equation by i. Hence

$$i^2 = \frac{a_0 i}{2} + \sum_{n=1}^{\infty}(a_n i \cos n\omega t + b_n i \sin n\omega t)$$

Hence

$$I_{\text{rms}}^2 = \frac{1}{T}\int_0^T \frac{a_0 i}{2}\,\mathrm{d}t$$

$$+ \sum_{n=1}^{\infty}\left[\frac{1}{T}\int_0^T a_n i \cos n\omega t\,\mathrm{d}t + \frac{1}{T}\int_0^T b_n i \sin n\omega t\,\mathrm{d}t\right] \qquad [7]$$

Since we have (chapter 2 equation [16])

$$a_0 = \frac{2}{T}\int_0^T i\,\mathrm{d}t$$

then the first integral term in equation [7] has the value of $a_0^2/4$. We also have (chapter 2 equation [18])

$$a_n = \frac{2}{T}\int_0^T i \cos n\omega t\,\mathrm{d}t$$

and (chapter 2 equation [20])

$$b_n = \frac{2}{T}\int_0^T i \sin n\omega t\,\mathrm{d}t$$

Thus the second term in equation [7] becomes

$$\sum_{n=0}^{n=\infty} \tfrac{1}{2}(a_n^2 + b_n^2)$$

Hence we can write equation [7] as

$$I_{\mathrm{rms}}^2 = \tfrac{1}{2}\left[\tfrac{1}{2}a_0^2 + \sum_{n=0}^{\infty} (a_n^2 + b_n^2)\right] \qquad [8]$$

The term *Parseval's theorem* is used for the relationship, which was derived above, of

$$\frac{2}{T}\int_0^T [f(t)]^2\,\mathrm{d}t = \tfrac{1}{2}a_0^2 + \sum_{n=0}^{\infty} (a_n^2 + b_n^2) \qquad [9]$$

We can write the Fourier series for the current in the form (chapter 2 equation [6]) as

$$i = A_0 + \sum_{n=0}^{\infty} A_n \sin(n\omega t + \phi_n)$$

where $A_0 = a_0/2$, $A_n = \sqrt{(a_n^2 + b_n^2)}$ (chapter 2 equation [9]) and $\phi_n = \tan^{-1}(a_n/b_n)$ (chapter 2 equation 10]). Thus if we have a current with amplitudes of I_1, I_2, I_3, etc. for each of the harmonics and I_0 for the d.c. term, then equation [8] can be written as

$$I_{\mathrm{rms}}^2 = I_0^2 + \tfrac{1}{2}\left[I_1^2 + I_2^2 + I_3^2 + \ldots\right] \qquad [10]$$

We could also derive the comparable equation for voltages.

$$V_{\mathrm{rms}}^2 = V_0^2 + \tfrac{1}{2}\left[V_1^2 + V_2^2 + V_3^2 + \ldots\right] \qquad [11]$$

Since the power developed by a current harmonic is $I_{\mathrm{rms}}^2 R$, and that by a voltage harmonic is V_{rms}^2/R, then the total power developed by a waveform is equal to the sum of the powers due to each harmonic acting independently.

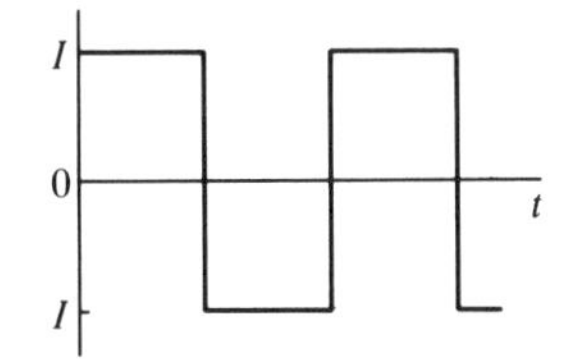

Fig. 6.6 Example

Example

Determine the root-mean-square value, and the percentage of the power in each harmonic, for a current which has the rectangular waveform shown in figure 6.6 and is described by

$$i = \frac{4I}{\pi}\left(\sin \omega t + \frac{1}{3}\sin 3\omega t + \frac{1}{5}\sin 5\omega t + \ldots\right)$$

A consideration of the form of the graph in figure 6.6 indicates that the we must have, over a period,

$$I_{\text{rms}}^2 = I^2$$

and thus the root-mean-square current due to all the harmonics is $I/\sqrt{2}$.

There is no d.c. component and only components at odd value harmonics. The root-mean-square current due to the first harmonic is

$$I_{\text{rms}}^2 = \frac{1}{2}\left(\frac{4I}{\pi}\right)^2 = 0.811I^2$$

Thus, since the average power is $I_{\text{rms}}^2 R$, there is 81.1% of the power contained in the first harmonic. The root-mean-square current due to the third harmonic is

$$I_{\text{rms}}^2 = \frac{1}{2}\left(\frac{4I}{\pi} \times \frac{1}{3}\right)^2 = 0.090I^2$$

Thus there is 9.0% of the power contained in the third harmonic. The root-mean-square current due to the fifth harmonic is

$$I_{\text{rms}}^2 = \frac{1}{2}\left(\frac{4I}{\pi} \times \frac{1}{5}\right)^2 = 0.032I^2$$

There is thus 3.2% of the power contained in the fifth harmonic.

Review problems

9 Determine the root-mean-square voltage when a voltage of the following form is applied to a circuit:

$$v = 100 \sin 500t + 40 \sin 1000t + 20 \sin 1500t \text{ V}$$

10 Determine the root-mean-square current when a current of the following form flows in a circuit:

$$i = 20 \sin(1000t - 15^\circ) + 3.5 \sin(3000t - 34^\circ) \text{ mA}$$

6.3 Power and power factor

When a voltage v is applied to a circuit and the current is i then the instantaneous power is vi. The *mean power P* developed over one period T is thus

$$P = \frac{1}{T}\int_0^T vi \, dt \qquad [12]$$

If the voltage can be described by a Fourier series of the general form

$$v = V_1 \sin \omega t + V_2 \sin 2\omega t + V_3 \sin 3\omega t + \ldots$$

and the current by

$$i = I_1 \sin(\omega t + \theta_1) + I_2 \sin(2\omega t + \theta_2) + I_3 \sin(3\omega t + \theta_3) + \ldots$$

then we need to obtain the integral of the product vi in order to obtain the mean power. If we consider the products of the terms due to each of the voltage and current harmonics, then integrated over a period we find that all those terms resulting from the product of different harmonics have zero value. For example, consider

$$\frac{1}{T}\int_0^T V_1 \sin \omega t \times I_2 \sin(2\omega t + \theta_2) \, dt$$

The relationship 2 sin A sin B = sin (A + B) + sin (A – B) enables the integral to be rewritten as

$$\frac{V_1 I_2}{2T}\int_0^T [\sin(3\omega t + \theta_2) - \sin(\omega t + \theta_2)] \, dt$$

Over a period, the area under the sin $(3\omega t + \theta_2)$ graph against time and that under the sin $(\omega t + \theta_2)$ graph, will be zero. Hence the term is zero. For the product of voltage and current terms for the same harmonic we have, for example,

$$\frac{1}{T}\int_0^T V_1 \sin \omega t \times I_1 \sin(\omega t + \theta_1) \, dt$$

Using the same angle relationship as above, then the integral can be written as

$$\frac{V_1 I_1}{2T}\int_0^T [\sin(2\omega t + \theta_1) - \sin \theta_1] \, dt$$

Over a period, the area under the sin $(2wt + \theta_1)$ graph against time will be zero. Thus the integral becomes

$$\frac{V_1 I_1}{2T}[t \cos \theta_1]_0^T = V_1 I_1 \cos \theta_1$$

Hence

$$P = V_1 I_1 \cos\theta_1 + V_2 I_2 \cos\theta_2 + V_3 I_3 \cos\theta_3 + \ldots \qquad [13]$$

Thus the total power dissipated, i.e. the true power, is the sum of the powers dissipated at each harmonic plus that due to any d.c. term present.

The overall *power factor* is defined as being

$$\text{power factor} = \frac{\text{true power supplied}}{\text{apparent power}}$$

$$= \frac{V_1 I_1 \cos\theta_1 + V_2 I_2 \cos\theta_2 + \ldots}{V_{rms} I_{rms}} \qquad [14]$$

where V_{rms} and I_{rms} are the total root-mean-square voltage and current.

Example

Determine the total power supplied to a circuit and the overall power factor if the voltage applied to the circuit is

$$v = 10 \sin 500t + 4 \sin 1000t + 2 \sin (1500t + 15°) \text{ V}$$

and the resulting circuit current is

$$i = 0.60 \sin (500t - 80°) + 0.05 \sin (1500t - 15°) + 0.02 \sin (2500t - 60°) \text{ A}$$

The true power is the sum of the powers supplied at each harmonic. Thus

$$P = (10/\sqrt{2}) \times (0.60/\sqrt{2}) \cos 80° + (2/\sqrt{2}) \times (0.05/\sqrt{2}) \cos 15° + (2/\sqrt{2}) \times (0.02/\sqrt{2}) \cos \{15° - (-60°)\}$$

$$= 0.57 \text{ W}$$

The root-mean-square voltage is given by equation [11] as

$$V_{rms} = \sqrt{\tfrac{1}{2}[10^2 + 4^2 + 2^2]} = 7.75 \text{ V}$$

and the root-mean-square current is given by equation [10] as

$$I_{rms} = \sqrt{\tfrac{1}{2}[0.60^2 + 0.05^2 + 0.02^2]} = 0.43 \text{ A}$$

Hence the power factor is given by equation [14] as

$$\text{power factor} = \frac{0.57}{7.75 \times 0.43} = 0.17$$

Review problems

11 A voltage of

$$v = 60 \sin 500t + 15 \sin (1500t + 45°) \text{ V}$$

is applied to a circuit and results in a current of

$$i = 2 \sin (500t - 30°) + 0.3 \sin (1500t - 15°) \text{ A}$$

Determine the power developed in the circuit and the overall power factor.

12 The voltage applied to a circuit is given by

$$v = 100 \sin 500t + 20 \sin (1500t + 45°) + 5 \sin (2500t - 30°) \text{ V}$$

and gives rise to a current of

$$i = 0.4 \sin (500t + 85°) + 0.2 \sin (1500t + 45°) + 0.05 \sin (2500t - 50°) \text{ A}$$

Determine the power developed and the overall power factor.

Further problems

13 A voltage of

$$v = 0.5 + 0.32 \sin 500t + 0.16 \sin 1000t + 0.11 \sin 1500t \text{ V}$$

is applied across a circuit of resistance 1000 Ω. What will be the waveform of the circuit current?

14 If the voltage waveform in the previous problem had been applied across a 10 μF capacitor, what would have been the reactances at each harmonic?

15 A circuit consists of a resistance R in series with an inductance L. Determine the circuit current when a rectangular voltage waveform of the following form is applied to it. The period is T.

$v = V_m$ for $0 \le t < T/2$
$v = 0$ for $T/2 \le t < T$

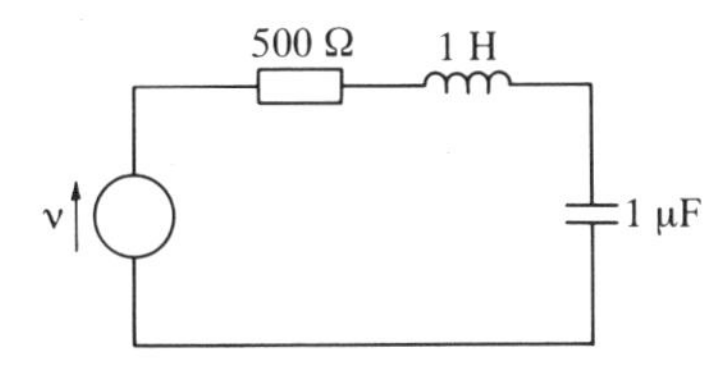

Fig. 6.7 Problem 16

16 For the circuit shown in figure 6.7, determine the current waveform when the applied voltage has the waveform

$$v = 20 \sin 500t + 4 \sin 1500t \text{ V}$$

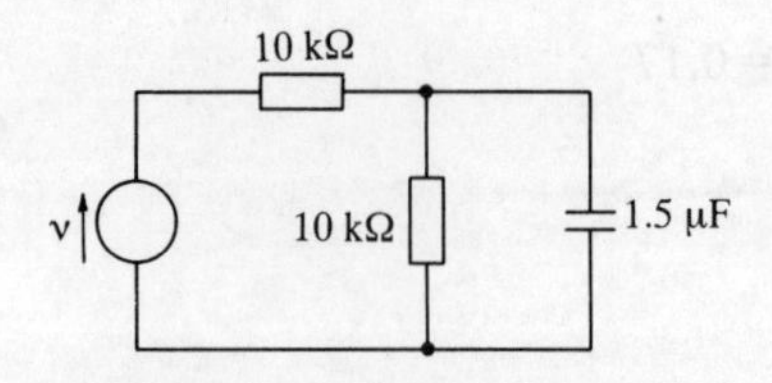

Fig. 6.8 Problem 17

17 For the circuit shown in figure 6.8, determine the waveform of the current taken from the source when the applied voltage has a waveform of the following form:

$v = 10$ V for $0 \le t < 50$ ms
$v = 0$ for 50 ms $\le t < 100$ ms, period = 100 ms

18 Determine the root-mean-square current when a current of the following form flows in a circuit.

$$i = 0.5 \sin (1000t - 0.45) + 0.1 \sin (3000t - 0.25) \text{ A}$$

19 Determine the root-mean-square voltage due to the first three terms for a rectangular waveform voltage which is described by the following Fourier series:

$$v = \frac{4}{\pi}\left(\sin \omega t + \frac{1}{3}\sin 3\omega t + \frac{1}{5}\sin 5\omega t + \dots\right) \text{ V}$$

20 Determine the root-mean-square current for a current described by the following Fourier series:

$$i = 1 + 10 \sin 500t + 8 \sin (1500t + 30°) + 3 \sin (2500t + 60°) \text{ mA}$$

21 A voltage with a rectangular waveform of

$$v = 15 + 27 \cos (500t - 45°) + 19 \cos (1000t - 90°) \text{ V}$$

is applied across a resistance of 15 Ω. Determine the power developed.

22 A half-wave rectified voltage waveform with a maximum value of 100 V is applied to a circuit consisting of a coil with an inductance of 10 mH and a resistance of 10 Ω. Determine the power dissipated in the circuit and the overall power factor.

23 A voltage which can be described by

$$v = 1 \sin 500t + 0.5 \sin 1500t \text{ V}$$

is applied to a circuit consisting of a resistance of 10 Ω in series with an inductance of 10 mH. Determine the power dissipated in the circuit.

24 A voltage which can be described by

$$v = 200 \sin \omega t + 50 \sin (3\omega t + 45°) + 15 \sin (5\omega t + 30°) \text{ V}$$

is applied to a circuit consisting of a resistance of 100 Ω in series with an inductance having an inductive reactance at the fundamental frequency of 100 Ω. Determine the power dissipated in the circuit.

25 A voltage which can be described by

$$v = 30 + 40 \sin 1000t + 25 \sin 2000t + 15 \sin 4000t \text{ V}$$

is applied to a circuit consisting of a resistance of 20 Ω in series with a capacitance of 20 μF. Determine the power dissipated in the circuit and the power factor.

26 A voltage which can be described by

$$v = 20 \sin \omega t + 10 \sin (3\omega t + \pi/4) + 5 \sin (5\omega t - \pi/2) \text{ V}$$

is applied to a circuit and results in a current of

$$i = 0.5 \sin (\omega t - \pi/6) + 0.1 \sin (3\omega t - \pi/12) + 0.05 \sin (5\omega t - 2\pi/3) \text{ A}$$

Determine the total power supplied and the overall power factor of the circuit.

27 Consider the current i and the voltage v defined over a period T by relationships of the form

$$f(t) = \tfrac{1}{2}a_0 + \sum_{n=1}^{\infty} (a_n \cos n\omega t + b_n \sin n\omega t)$$

Hence determine the product iv and so the average value of iv as

$$\tfrac{1}{4}a_{i0}a_{vo} + \tfrac{1}{2}\sum_{n=1}^{\infty} (a_{in}a_{vn} + b_{in}b_{vn})$$

Hint: determine $i(t) + v(t)$ and $i(t) - v(t)$ and then by Parseval's theorem the integral of $\{i(t) + v(t)\}^2$ and $\{i(t) - v(t)\}^2$. The difference between these quantities gives 4 times the integral of the required product.

7 Numerical harmonic analysis

7.1 Numerical integration

In practical situations a waveform is generally obtained in the form of a set of readings of y at a number of different times t, or as a trace on a cathode ray oscilloscope screen, rather than as an algebraic expression. Direct integration to determine the Fourier coefficients is then not possible and thus numerical methods of integration have to be used. Since such an analysis enables the harmonics of a waveform to be determined, it is often referred to as *harmonic analysis*.

7.1.1 Trapezium rule

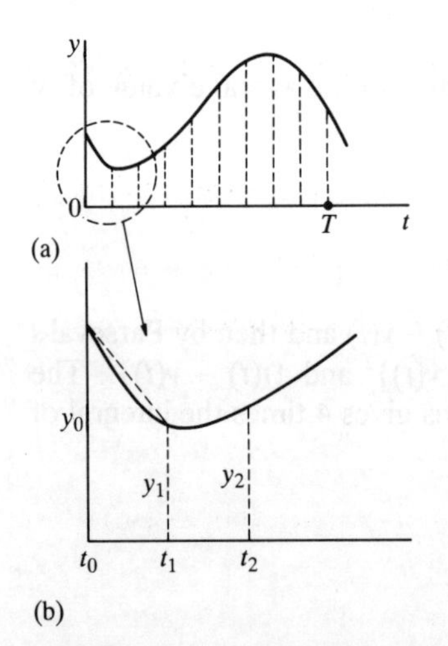

Fig. 7.1 The trapezium rule

Essentially, the integration of a function between two limits can be considered to be essentially the determination of the area under a graph of the function between those limits. A simple method that is often used is called the *trapezium rule*. Consider the function $y = f(t)$ which is described by the graph shown in figure 7.1(a). The function is a periodic one which repeats itself every period T. The area under the graph between the limits, say 0 and T, is subdivided into a number of strips. Each such strip is then considered to be in the form of a trapezium, as shown in figure 7.1(b). This is a strip with the upper end being a straight line drawn between the endpoints of that part of the curve for the strip. The area of a trapezium is its average height times the base. Thus the area of the first strip in figure 7.1(b) is

$$\text{area} = \frac{y_0 + y_1}{2} \times (t_1 - t_0)$$

If T is the period of the function then if the interval between 0 and T is divided into k equal width strips, each strip will have a width of T/k. Therefore, the total area A under the graph of the waveform between 0 and T is approximately

$$A \approx \frac{1}{2}(y_0 + y_1)\frac{T}{k} + \frac{1}{2}(y_1 + y_2)\frac{T}{k} + \frac{1}{2}(y_2 + y_3)\frac{T}{k} + \dots$$
$$+ \frac{1}{2}(y_{k-2} + y_{k-1})\frac{T}{k} + \frac{1}{2}(y_{k-1} + y_k)\frac{T}{k}$$

This can be written as

$$A \approx \frac{T}{2k}(y_0 + y_1 + y_1 + y_2 + y_2 + \dots + y_{k-1} + y_{k-1} + y_k)$$

$$\approx \frac{T}{2k}\left\{\frac{1}{2}(y_0 + y_k) + 2y_1 + 2y_2 + \dots + 2y_{k-1}\right\}$$

Since the waveform is considered to be periodic then its starting value y_0 is the same as its finishing value y_k at the end of a period. Thus

$$\int_0^T y\,dt = A \approx \frac{T}{k}(y_0 + y_1 + y_2 + \dots + y_{k-1}) \qquad [1]$$

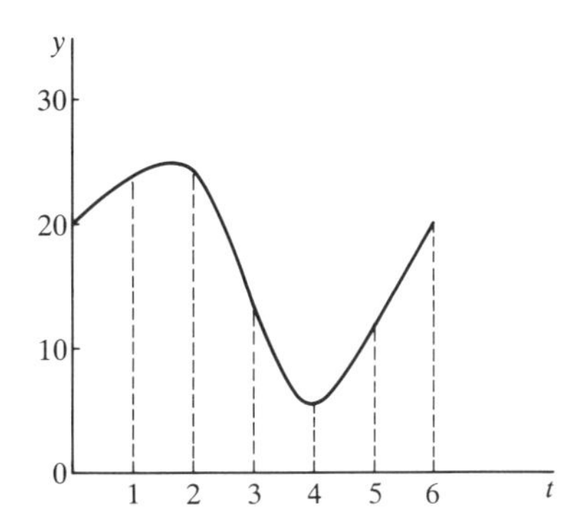

Fig. 7.2 Example

Example

Estimate, by numerical integration, the value of the integral

$$\int_0^6 y\,dt$$

for the graph of the periodic function, period = 6 s, shown in figure 7.2, when the area is divided into six strips.

The integral is the area under the graph and is given approximately by equation [1] as

$$\int_0^6 y\,dt \approx \frac{6}{6}(20 + 24 + 24 + 13 + 6 + 12) \approx 99 \text{ square units}$$

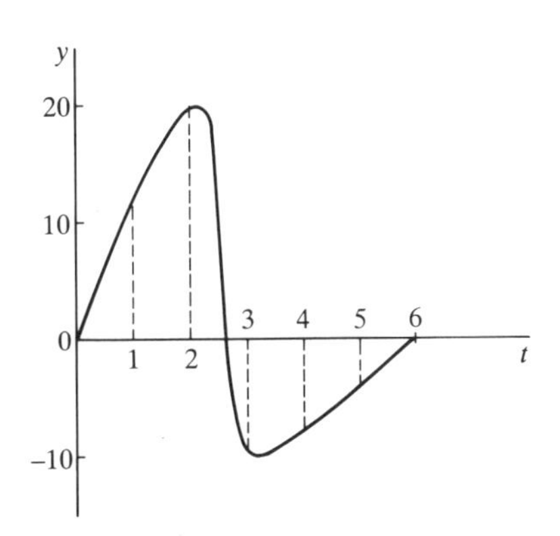

Fig. 7.3 Problem 1

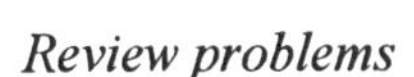
Review problems

1 Estimate, by numerical integration, the value of the integral

$$\int_0^6 y\,dt$$

for the graph of the periodic function, period = 6 s, shown in figure 7.3, when the area is divided into six strips.

2 Estimate, by numerical integration, the integral

$$\int_0^8 y\,dt$$

for a periodic function, period = 8 s, which has the following function values:

y	2	4	1	−2	−3	−2	0	1
t	0	1	2	3	4	5	6	7

7.2 Harmonic analysis

Consider the representation of a waveform, which cannot be directly integrated, by a Fourier series and the determination of the Fourier coefficients. Since we have (chapter 2 equation [16])

$$a_0 = \frac{2}{T}\int_0^T y\,dt$$

then we must have when numerically integrating, using equation [1],

$$a_0 \approx \frac{2}{k}(y_0 + y_1 + y_2 + \ldots + y_{k-1}) \qquad [2]$$

The coefficient a_n is given by (chapter 2 equation [18])

$$a_n = \frac{2}{T}\int_0^T y \cos n\omega t\,dt$$

Since $\omega = 2\pi/T$ then we can write, using equation [1],

$$a_n \approx \frac{2}{k}\left(y_0 \cos\frac{2\pi n}{T}t_0 + y_1 \cos\frac{2\pi n}{T}t_1 + \ldots + y_{k-1}\cos\frac{2\pi n}{T}t_{k-1}\right) \qquad [3]$$

For the coefficient b_n we have (chapter 2 equation [20]),

$$b_n = \frac{2}{T}\int_0^T y \sin n\omega t\,dt$$

and so

$$b_n \approx \frac{2}{k}\left(y_0 \sin\frac{2\pi n}{T}t_0 + y_1 \sin\frac{2\pi n}{T}t_1 + \ldots + y_{k-1}\sin\frac{2\pi n}{T}t_{k-1}\right) \qquad [4]$$

In the above discussion the coefficients have been found for a waveform for which the period is T. Often the analysis is carried out for a period of 2π. This simplifies the expressions and the resulting calculations since the cosines and sines become just of the product nt rather than $2\pi nt/T$. The effect is of presenting the period on a different time scale and to convert a graph of a waveform with period 2π to one with period T. All that is required is to change the time scale so that the period is T rather than 2π.

7.2.1 Twelve-point analysis

An important consideration when carrying out the numerical integration of a periodic waveform is to how many strips the period should be divided into for the determination of the area. In general, with numerical integration, the more strips that are taken the greater the accuracy that is possible. However, consider a waveform which has harmonics. Suppose it has a fifth harmonic expressed as a sine. This means that every 1/10th of the fundamental period the harmonic has a zero value. Thus if we divide the fundamental period into ten equal size strips, we can obtain no information about the fifth harmonic since the ordinates of each strip will have the value 0. Harmonic analysis carried out up to the fifth harmonic thus requires more strips than 10. Since, for many purposes analysis need only be carried out up to the fifth harmonic, 12 equal size strips are generally used and the analysis referred to as *twelve-point analysis*. 12 has the advantage of dividing a period of 2π or 360° into 'nice' segments of $\pi/6$ or 30°. In general, to determine n harmonics, at least $2n + 1$ strips must be considered. If analysis needs to be carried out beyond the fifth harmonic, either more strips can be used or the waveform due to the first five harmonics subtracted and the twelve-point analysis repeated for the residue waveform.

With twelve-point analysis there are many calculations involved and a lot of data. The analysis can be greatly helped by setting out the calculations in a table. The example that follows shows such a table. The work is also simplified by a consideration of the symmetry of the waveform in order to determine which harmonics are not present.

Example

Determine the Fourier series for the periodic waveform shown in figure 7.4 and which has the following function values y at intervals of $t = \pi/6$ or 30°:

y	10	12	24	26	24	20	16	14	12	8	6	8	10
$t°$	0	30	60	90	120	150	180	210	240	270	300	330	360

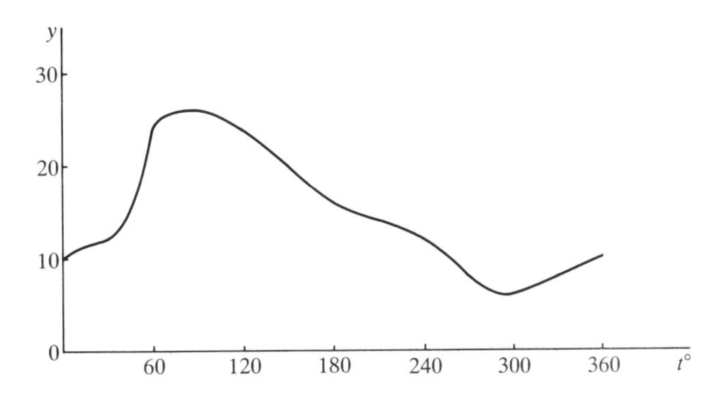

Fig. 7.4 Example

Using equation [2] we can obtain a_0.

$$a_0 \approx \tfrac{2}{12}(y_0 + y_1 + y_2 + \dots + y_{k-1})$$

$$\approx \tfrac{1}{6}(10 + 12 + 24 + 26 + 24 + 20 + 16 + 14 + 12 + 8 + 6 + 8)$$

Thus a_0 has an approximate value of 30.

We can use equation [3] to find the value of a_1.

$$a_1 \approx \tfrac{2}{12}(y_0 \cos t_0 + y_1 \cos t_1 + \dots + y_{k-1} \cos t_{k-1})$$

$$\approx \tfrac{1}{6}(10 + 12\cos 30^\circ + 24\cos 60^\circ + 26\cos 90^\circ + 24\cos 120^\circ + 20\cos 150^\circ + 16\cos 180^\circ + 14\cos 210^\circ + 12\cos 240^\circ + 8\cos 270^\circ + 6\cos 300^\circ + 8\cos 330^\circ)$$

$$\approx \tfrac{1}{6}(10 + 10.44 + 12 + 0 - 12 - 17.4 - 16 - 12.18 - 6 + 0 + 3 + 6.96)$$

Thus a_1 has an approximate value of -3.53.

We can use equation [3] to find the value of a_2.

$$a_2 \approx \tfrac{2}{12}(y_0 \cos 2t_0 + y_1 \cos 2t_1 + \dots + y_{k-1} \cos 2t_{k-1})$$

$$\approx \tfrac{1}{6}(10 + 12\cos 60^\circ + 24\cos 120^\circ + 26\cos 180^\circ + 24\cos 240^\circ + 20\cos 300^\circ + 16\cos 360^\circ + 14\cos 420^\circ + 12\cos 480^\circ + 8\cos 540^\circ + 6\cos 600^\circ + 8\cos 660^\circ)$$

$$\approx \tfrac{1}{6}(10 + 6 - 12 - 26 - 12 + 10 + 16 + 7 - 6 - 8 - 3 + 4)$$

Thus a_2 has an approximate value of -2.33.

We can use equation [4] to find the value of b_1.

$$b_1 \approx \tfrac{2}{12}(y_0 \sin t_0 + y_1 \sin t_1 + \dots + y_{k-1} \sin t_{k-1})$$

$$\approx \tfrac{1}{6}(0 + 12\sin 30^\circ + 24\sin 60^\circ + 26\sin 90^\circ + 24\sin 120^\circ + 20\sin 150^\circ + 16\sin 180^\circ + 14\sin 210^\circ + 12\sin 240^\circ + 8\sin 270^\circ + 6\sin 300^\circ + 8\sin 330^\circ)$$

$$\approx \tfrac{1}{6}(0 + 6 + 20.88 + 26 + 20.88 + 10 + 0 - 7 - 10.44 - 8 - 5.22 - 4)$$

Thus b_1 is approximately 8.18.

We can use equation [4] to determine b_2.

$$b_2 \approx \tfrac{2}{12}(y_0 \sin 2t_0 + y_1 \sin 2t_1 + \ldots + y_{k-1} \sin 2t_{k-1})$$

$$\approx \tfrac{1}{6}(0 + 12 \sin 60^\circ + 24 \sin 120^\circ + 26 \sin 180^\circ + 24 \sin 240^\circ + 20 \sin 300^\circ + 16 \sin 360^\circ + 14 \sin 420^\circ + 12 \sin 480^\circ + 8 \sin 540^\circ + 6 \sin 600^\circ + 8 \sin 660^\circ)$$

$$\approx \tfrac{1}{6}(0 + 10.44 + 20.88 + 0 - 20.88 - 17.4 + 0 + 12.18 + 10.44 + 0 - 5.22 - 6.96)$$

Thus b_2 is approximately 0.58.

The above analysis can be repeated for the Fourier coefficients for the third, fourth and fifth harmonics. Table 7.1 shows these calculations, for the first three harmonics, laid out in a systematic form in a table. The result is the Fourier series

$$y = 15 - 3.53 \cos t - 2.33 \cos 2t + 8.18 \sin t + 0.58 \sin 2t - 1.33 \sin 3t$$

Table 7.1 Determination of the Fourier coefficients
(a) cosine terms

t°	y	$\cos t$	$y \cos t$	$\cos 2t$	$y \cos 2t$	$\cos 3t$	$y \cos 3t$
0	10	1	10	1	10	1	10
30	12	0.87	10.44	0.5	6	0	0
60	24	0.5	12	−0.5	−12	−1	−24
90	26	0	0	−1	−26	0	0
120	24	−0.5	−12	−0.5	−12	1	24
150	20	−0.87	−17.4	0.5	10	0	0
180	16	−1	−16	1	16	−1	−16
210	14	−0.87	−12.18	0.5	7	0	0
240	12	−0.5	−6	−0.5	−6	1	12
270	8	0	0	−1	−8	0	0
300	6	0.5	3	−0.5	−3	−1	−6
330	8	0.87	6.96	0.5	4	0	0
	$\sum y = 180$		$\sum y \cos t = -21.18$		$\sum y \cos 2t = -14$		$\sum y \cos 3t = 0$
	$a_0 = 30$		$a_1 = -3.53$		$a_2 = -2.33$		$a_3 = 0$

(b) sine terms

t^o	y	$\sin t$	$y \sin t$	$\sin 2t$	$y \sin 2t$	$\sin 3t$	$y \sin 3t$
0	10	0	0	0	0	0	0
30	12	0.5	6	0.87	10.44	1	12
60	24	0.87	20.88	0.87	20.88	0	0
90	26	1	26	0	0	−1	−26
120	24	0.87	20.88	−0.87	−20.88	0	0
150	20	0.5	10	−0.87	−17.4	1	20
180	16	0	0	0	0	0	0
210	14	−0.5	−7	0.87	12.18	−1	−14
240	12	−0.87	−10.44	0.87	10.44	0	0
270	8	−1	−8	0	0	1	8
300	6	−0.87	−5.22	−0.87	−5.22	0	0
330	8	−0.5	−4	−0.87	−6.96	−1	−8
			$\sum y \sin t = 49.1$		$\sum y \sin 2t = 3.48$		$\sum y \sin 3t = -8$
			$b_1 = 8.18$		$b_2 = 0.58$		$b_3 = -1.33$

Review problems

3 By the use of twelve-point analysis, determine the first three harmonics in the Fourier series for a periodic current waveform which gave the following points within one period:

i	67	222	163	53	47	72	33
t^o	0	30	60	90	120	150	180

i	−22	−63	−153	−247	−172
t^o	210	240	270	300	330

4 By the use of twelve-point analysis, determine the first three harmonics in the Fourier series for a periodic waveform which gave the following points within one period:

y	30	40	46	48	40	16	6
t^o	0	30	60	90	120	150	180

y	8	18	24	20	22
t^o	210	240	270	300	330

5 By the use of twelve-point analysis, determine the first three harmonics in the Fourier series for a periodic waveform which gave the following points within one period:

y	1.2	10.4	9.9	7.0	9.9	10.4	1.2
t^o	0	30	60	90	120	150	180

y	−8.0	−7.5	−4.6	−7.5	−8.0
t^o	210	240	270	300	330

6 By the use of twelve-point analysis, determine the first three harmonics in the Fourier series for a periodic waveform which gave the following points within one period:

y	36.0	31.2	21.5	15.0	13.5	13.8	14.0
t^o	0	30	60	90	120	150	180

y	13.8	13.5	15.0	21.5	31.2
t^o	210	240	270	300	330

7 By the use of twelve-point analysis, determine the first three harmonics in the Fourier series for a periodic waveform which gave the following points within one period:

y	11.0	17.7	12.7	6.0	12.7	0.3	−11
t^o	0	30	60	90	120	150	180

y	−17.7	−12.7	−6.0	−14.7	0.3
t^o	210	240	270	300	330

Further problems

8 By the use of twelve-point analysis, determine the first three harmonics in the Fourier series for the following periodic current waveform and compare the result with that given in table 2.1:

$y = 1$ for $0 \leq t < \pi$
$y = -1$ for $\pi \leq t < 2\pi$, period $= 2\pi$

9 By the use of twelve-point analysis, determine the first three harmonics in the Fourier series for a periodic displacement waveform which gave the following points within one period:

y	20	44	62	58	55	48	47
t^o	0	30	60	90	120	150	180

y	43	40	30	25	23
t^o	210	240	270	300	330

10 By the use of twelve-point analysis, determine the first three harmonics in the Fourier series for a periodic current waveform which gave the following points within one period:

i	0	480	670	550	364	260	0
t°	0	30	60	90	120	150	180

i	−480	−670	−550	−364	−260
t°	210	240	270	300	330

11 By the use of twelve-point analysis, determine the first three harmonics in the Fourier series for the waveform described by figure 7.5.

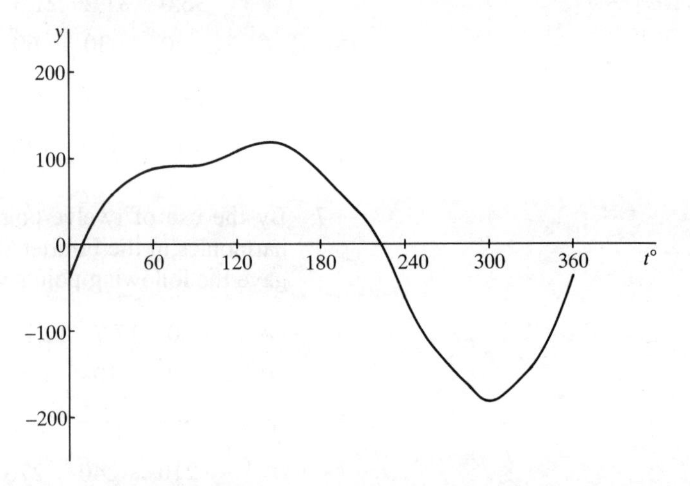

Fig. 7.5 Problem 11

12 By the use of twelve-point analysis, determine the first four harmonics in the Fourier series for the waveform described by figure 7.6.

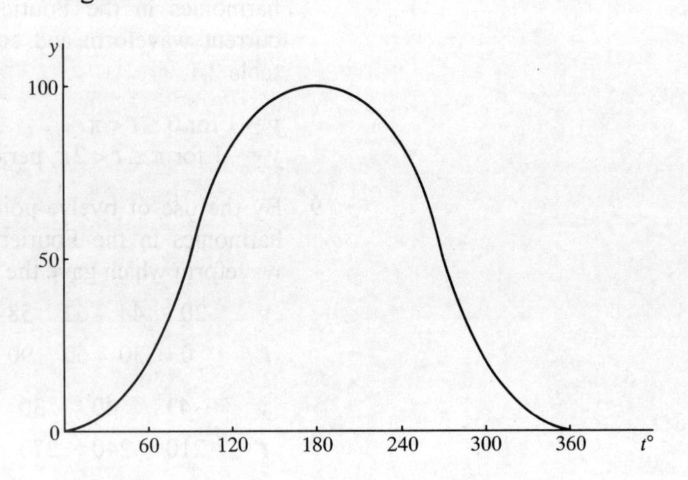

Fig. 7.6 Problem 12

8 Ordinary differential equations

8.1 Differentiation and integration

In chapter 6 electrical circuits were analysed when subject to inputs of voltages in the form of rectangular, triangular, half-wave rectified sinusoids, etc. waveforms. The principle of regarding each harmonic in the waveform separately and then using the *principle of superposition* to determine the total effect was used. This, in essence, relied on the ability to differentiate or integrate each harmonic independently. In this chapter, differentiation and integration of Fourier series are considered and its application in the solution of differential equations describing systems where there is an input which is represented by a Fourier series. The main applications discussed in this chapter involve mechanical systems, though the methods, as illustrated by chapter 6, are equally applicable to electrical systems.

8.1.1 Differentiation

If some function $y = f(t)$ can be accurately represented by a Fourier series then it seems feasible to expect that if we can differentiate the function we should be able to differentiate the series. In fact, we can differentiate a Fourier series term-by-term and end up with a series which describes the differentiated function, provided the series converges. This does not always occur. For the differentiated series $\mathrm{d}f(t)/\mathrm{d}t$ to converge, it must satisfy the Dirichlet conditions (see section 2.2.1), i.e. only one value of $\mathrm{d}f(t)/\mathrm{d}t$ for each value of t. Also, $\mathrm{d}f(t)/\mathrm{d}t$ must be continuous or piecewise continuous within the periodic interval.

To illustrate this, consider the periodic rectangular waveform shown in figure 8.1. The period is 2π. The Fourier series for the waveform is (table 2.1 item 2)

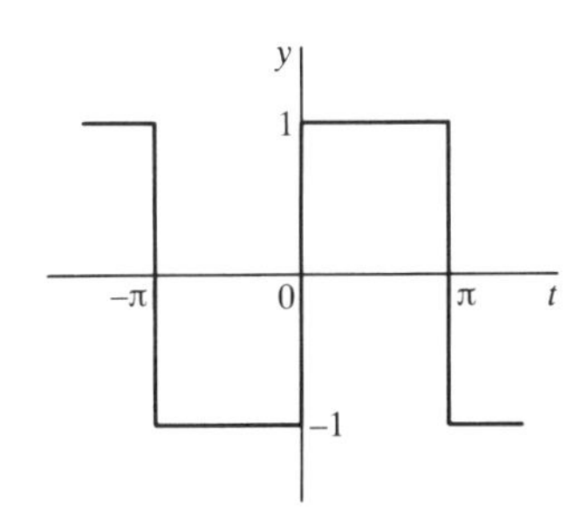

Fig. 8.1 Rectangular waveform

$$y = f(t) = \frac{4}{\pi}\left(\sin t + \frac{1}{3}\sin 3t + \frac{1}{5}\sin 5t + \dots\right)$$

The series converges with successive terms being smaller and smaller. If we differentiate the series term-by-term then

$$\frac{dy}{dx} = \frac{4}{\pi}(-\cos t - \cos 3t - \cos 5t - \ldots)$$

This series does not converge and thus does not give a valid value of dy/dt.

In general, for a Fourier series for the function $y = f(t)$ in the form

$$y = \tfrac{1}{2}a_0 + \sum_{n=1}^{n=\infty} (a_n \cos n\omega t + b_n \sin n\omega t)$$

we have, on differentiating this function term-by-term,

$$\frac{dy}{dx} = \sum_{n=1}^{n=\infty} (-n\omega a_n \sin n\omega t + n\omega b_n \cos n\omega t) \qquad [1]$$

Example

Differentiate the Fourier series representing the triangular wave function

$$y = f(t) = -t \text{ for } -\pi \le t < 0$$
$$y = f(t) = t \text{ for } 0 \le t < \pi, \text{ period} = 2\pi$$

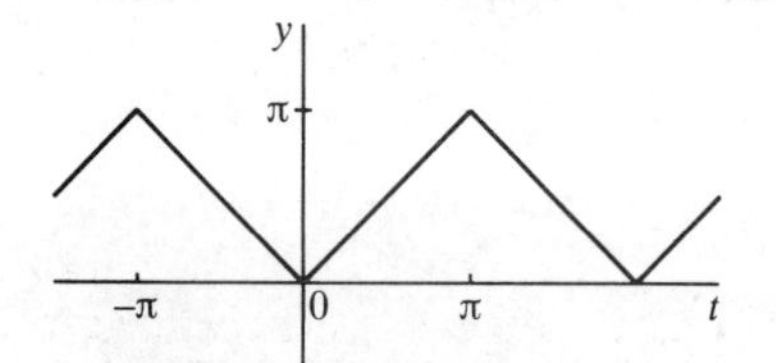

Fig. 8.2 Example

Figure 8.2 shows the function. Using table 2.1, item 4, the Fourier series for the function is

$$y = \frac{\pi}{2} - \frac{4}{\pi}\left(-\cos t + \frac{1}{9}\cos 3t - \frac{1}{25}\cos 5t + \ldots\right)$$

Differentiating term-by-term, this series gives

$$\frac{dy}{dt} = -\frac{4}{\pi}\left(-\sin t + \frac{1}{3}\sin 3t - \frac{1}{5}\sin 5t - \ldots\right)$$

We can visualise the form of the differentiated waveform by considering that, when differentiating the function, all we are doing is considering how the gradient of the waveform changes.

Since for the interval $-\pi \le t < 0$ the slope of the graph of the waveform is constant at $\pi/(-\pi)$ then dy/dt for this interval is -1. For the interval $0 \le t < \pi$ the slope of the graph is constant at π/π and so for this interval $dy/dt = +1$. Thus the above Fourier series for dy/dt describes the waveform shown in figure 8.3.

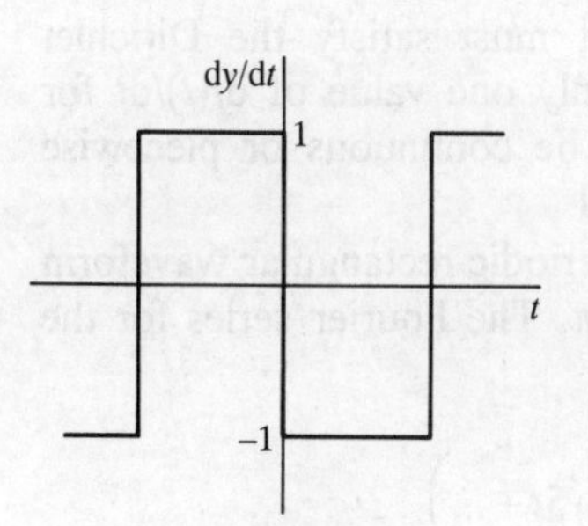

Fig. 8.3 Example

Review problems

1 Differentiate the function which has the following Fourier series and indicate whether the result is valid.

$$y = \frac{4}{\pi} - \frac{2}{\pi}\left(\frac{1}{3}\cos t + \frac{1}{15}\cos 2t + \ldots\right)$$

2 Differentiate the Fourier series for the function giving the waveform described by

$$y = f(t) = -4t \text{ for } -\pi \le t < 0$$
$$y = f(t) = +4t \text{ for } 0 \le t < \pi, \text{ period} = 2\pi$$

and indicate whether the result is valid.

8.1.2 Integration

A Fourier series can always be integrated term-by-term to obtain a further, valid, Fourier series. Thus if we have the general form for the Fourier series of a function $y = f(t)$ of

$$y = \tfrac{1}{2}a_0 + \sum_{n=1}^{n=\infty} (a_n \cos n\omega t + b_n \sin n\omega t)$$

then

$$\int_0^t y\,dt = \tfrac{1}{2}a_0 t + \sum_{n=1}^{n=\infty} \frac{1}{n\omega}[a_n \sin n\omega t - b_n(\cos n\omega t - 1)] \qquad [2]$$

Example

Integrate, between t and 0, the Fourier series for the rectangular waveform described by figure 8.1.

The waveform has the Fourier series (see table 2.1 item 2) of

$$y = f(t) = \frac{4}{\pi}\left(\sin t + \frac{1}{3}\sin 3t + \frac{1}{5}\sin 5t + \ldots\right)$$

Integrating term-by-term gives

$$\int_0^t y\,dt = \frac{4}{\pi}\int_0^t \sin t\,dt + \frac{4}{\pi}\int_0^t \frac{1}{3}\sin 3t\,dt + \frac{4}{\pi}\int_0^t \frac{1}{5}\sin 5t\,dt + \ldots$$

$$= \frac{4}{\pi}[-\cos t]_0^t + \frac{4}{\pi}\left[-\frac{1}{9}\cos 3t\right]_0^t + \frac{4}{\pi}\left[-\frac{1}{25}\cos 5t\right]_0^t + \ldots$$

$$= -\frac{4}{\pi}(\cos t + 1) - \frac{4}{9\pi}(\cos 3t + 1) - \frac{4}{25\pi}(\cos 5t + 1) - \ldots$$

Review problems

3 Integrate term-by-term the Fourier series

$$y = f(t) = 2\left(\sin t - \frac{1}{2}\sin 2t + \frac{1}{3}\sin 3t - \dots\right)$$

8.2 Ordinary differential equations

An equation involving derivatives is called a *differential equation*. Such equations are termed *ordinary differential equations* if they only contain derivatives involving the differentiation of a function with respect to a single variable. A general form of a *first-order* differential equation might be

$$a\frac{\mathrm{d}y}{\mathrm{d}t} + by = f(t) \qquad [3]$$

The equation is first-order because it contains, as its highest derivative, $\mathrm{d}y/\mathrm{d}t$. a and b are constants and $f(t)$ is some function of t which is applied to the system. Such a first-order differential equation might describe an electrical circuit involving an inductance and a resistance and subject to a voltage source connected to it. The function $f(t)$ would describe this voltage source and how its input varies with time t. This function is often referred to as the *forcing function.*

A *second-order* ordinary differential equation might be

$$a\frac{\mathrm{d}^2y}{\mathrm{d}t^2} + b\frac{\mathrm{d}y}{\mathrm{d}t} + cy = f(t) \qquad [4]$$

The equations is said to be second-order because it contains as its highest derivative $\mathrm{d}^2y/\mathrm{d}t^2$. a, b and c are constants and $f(t)$ is some function of t which is applied to the system, the so-called forcing function. Such an equation could describe the current oscillations occurring in a circuit containing resistance, capacitance and inductance when there is a voltage source connected to it. The function $f(t)$ would describe this voltage source and how its input varies with time t.

Such differential equations can be solved by considering the solution to be the sum of the solution of the corresponding homogeneous equation. That is the so-called *complementary function* y_c and another term called the *particular integral* y_p, i.e.

$$y = y_c + y_p$$

The corresponding *homogeneous* equation is the differential equation with the forcing function equal to 0. Thus, if we consider the second-order differential equation, this is

$$a\frac{d^2y}{dt^2}+b\frac{dy}{dt}+cy=0$$

The particular integral is obtained by considering the form of the forcing function. If the forcing function is a constant, i.e. not varying with time, then a constant A is tried for the particular integral.

To illustrate the above, consider the second-order differential equation

$$\frac{d^2y}{dt^2}-3\frac{dy}{dt}-4y=4$$

The homogeneous equation is

$$\frac{d^2y}{dt^2}-3\frac{dy}{dt}-4y=0$$

Trying a solution of the form $y = Ae^{st}$ gives, when substituted in the homogeneous differential equation, the auxiliary equation of

$$s^2Ae^{st} - 3sAe^{st} - 4Ae^{st} = 0$$

and so

$$s^2 - 3s - 4 = 0$$

$$(s + 1)(s - 4) = 0$$

Thus $s = -1$ or $+4$ and so

$$y_c = Ae^{-1t} + Be^{4t}$$

The constants A and B can be found using conditions such as, perhaps, $y = 0$ when $t = 0$ and $dy/dt = 0$ when $t = 0$.

For the particular integral, since the forcing function is a constant, we try $y = C$, where C is some constant. Using this value in the differential equation gives, since both d^2y/dt^2 and dy/dt are 0,

$$0 - 0 - 4C = 4$$

Thus $C = -1$. The full solution of the differential equation is thus

$$y = Ae^{-1t} + Be^{4t} - 1$$

If the forcing function $f(t)$ is a single sine or cosine function then $A \cos \omega t + B \sin \omega t$ is tried for the particular integral. We can think of the forcing function being a single harmonic and the particular integral also being a single harmonic, the same harmonic. Thus, suppose the differential equation had been

$$\frac{d^2y}{dt^2} - 3\frac{dy}{dt} - 4y = 3 \sin 2t$$

then the complementary function would be as above and we would try $C \cos 2t + D \sin 2t$ for the particular integral. Using this value gives, when substituted in the differential equation,

$$(-4C \cos 2t - 4D \sin 2t) - 3(-2C \sin 2t + 2D \cos 2t) - 4(C \cos 2t + D \sin 2t) = 3 \sin 2t$$

Equating the coefficients of cos $2t$ gives

$$-4C - 6D - 4C = 0$$

i.e. $8C = -6D$. Equating the coefficients of sin $2t$ gives

$$-4D + 6C - 4D = 3$$

Hence $C = 0.18$ and $D = -0.24$. Thus the particular integral is

$$y_p = 0.18 \cos 2t - 0.24 \sin 2t$$

The full solution is then

$$y = Ae^{-1t} + Be^{4t} + 0.18 \cos 2t - 0.24 \sin 2t$$

In the above differential equation, the forcing function was a simple single sine function, i.e. just one harmonic. If the forcing function is periodic and represented by a Fourier series, e.g. it might be a rectangular wave or a half-rectified sinusoid, then we have a number of sinusoids with different harmonics. Using the fact that we can differentiate term-by-term, i.e. the principle of superposition, we can regard each harmonic separately, derive a solution for each harmonic and then sum all the particular integrals to give the total particular integral. Thus, what we are doing is considering the particular integral to be tried to be

$$y_p = C_n \cos nt + D_n \sin nt$$

To illustrate this, consider the differential equation

$$\frac{d^2y}{dt^2} - 3\frac{dy}{dt} - 4y = 5 \sin t + 3 \sin 2t$$

This involves two harmonics. If we first consider the forcing function first harmonic term, then we can try $C \cos t + D \sin t$ for the particular integral. Substituting this value in the differential equation, when only the first harmonic term is present, gives

$$(-C \cos t - D \sin t) - 3(-C \sin t + D \cos t)$$
$$- 4(C \cos t + D \sin t) = 5 \sin t$$

Equating the coefficients of $\cos t$ gives

$$-C - 3D - 4C = 0$$

Thus $5C = -3D$. Equating the coefficients of $\sin t$ gives

$$-D + 3C - 4D = 5$$

Thus $C = -15/14$ and $D = 25/14$. The particular integral for the first harmonic is thus

$$y_p = -1.07 \cos t + 1.79 \sin t$$

The particular integral for the second harmonic was found earlier to be

$$y_p = 0.18 \cos 2t - 0.24 \sin 2t$$

Thus the full solution for the particular integral is

$$y_p = -1.07 \cos t + 1.79 \sin t + 0.18 \cos 2t - 0.24 \sin 2t$$

and so the full solution for the differential equation is

$$y = Ae^{-1t} + Be^{4t} - 1.07 \cos t + 1.79 \sin t + 0.18 \cos 2t$$
$$- 0.24 \sin 2t$$

The following are some general points about the solutions of homogeneous second-order differential equations, i.e. the complementary solutions of non-homogeneous, second-order differential equations. For an equation in the form

$$a\frac{d^2y}{dt^2} + by = 0 \qquad [5]$$

the solution is of the form

$$y = A \sin \sqrt{b/a}\, t + B \sin \sqrt{b/a}\, t \qquad [6]$$

For an equation in the form

$$a\frac{d^2y}{dt^2}+b\frac{dy}{dx}+cy=0 \qquad [7]$$

the solution with $b^2 > 4ac$, i.e. there are two real and distinct roots to the auxiliary equation, is of the form

$$y = Ae^{s_1 t} + Be^{s_2 t} \qquad [8]$$

where s_1 and s_2 are the roots of the auxiliary equation. The solution with $b^2 = 4ac$, i.e. the two roots are equal and real, is of the form

$$y = (At + B)e^{st} \qquad [9]$$

With $b^2 < 4ac$, i.e. the two roots are imaginary, the solution is of the form

$$y = e^{-\mu t}(A\cos\omega t + B\sin\omega t) \qquad [10]$$

with the roots being in the form of $s = -\mu \pm j\omega$ with $\mu = b/2a$ and $\omega = \sqrt{4ac - b^2}$.

Review problems

4 Solve the following differential equations:

(a) $\dfrac{d^2y}{dt^2} + 4y = \sin t$,

(b) $\dfrac{d^2y}{dt^2} + 4y = \sin t + \dfrac{1}{9}\sin 3t + \dfrac{1}{25}\sin 5t$

8.3 Mechanical oscillations

To illustrate the use of Fourier series with differential equations, in this section oscillating mechanical systems are analysed. Consider a mechanical system consisting of a mass m attached to the end of a tethered spring, as in figure 8.4. Such an arrangement can be considered to be a model for many mechanical systems. When the mass is pulled down a distance y then the spring is stretched by this amount. When the mass is released then, assuming that the spring obeys Hooke's law, there will be a restoring force exerted on the mass of $-ky$, where k is a constant called the spring stiffness. The minus sign is because the restoring force is in the opposite direction to that direction in which y increases. Newton's second law then gives

$$ma = m\frac{d^2y}{dt^2} = -ky$$

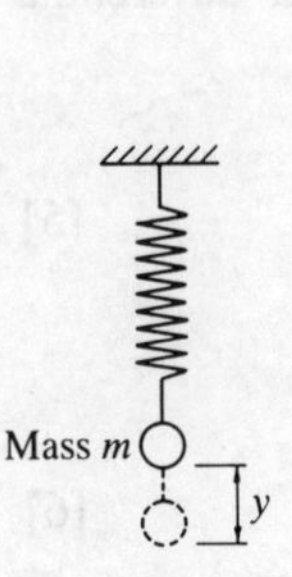

Fig. 8.4 Spring-mass system

with a being the acceleration of the mass. Thus the differential equation describing the motion of the mass is

$$m\frac{d^2y}{dt^2} + ky = 0 \qquad [11]$$

This is a homogeneous, second-order differential equation which describes the oscillations of an undamped mechanical system.

Now consider what happens if an external force $F(t)$ is applied to the system, e.g. the support of the spring may be being vibrated. The resultant force acting on the mass is now $F(t) - ky$. Newton's second law then gives

$$ma = m\frac{d^2y}{dt^2} = F(t) - ky$$

and so

$$m\frac{d^2y}{dt^2} + ky = F(t) \qquad [12]$$

This is a non-homogeneous, second-order differential equation which describes the forced oscillations of an undamped mechanical system.

Now consider a mechanical system when there is damping.

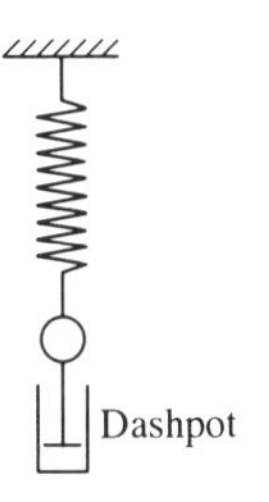

Fig. 8.5 Damped spring-mass system

The damping can be represented by a dashpot, as in figure 8.5. When the mass moves then the damping will result in a resistive force. Assuming that the damping force is proportional to the velocity v of the mass, the damping resistive force can written as cv or $c\,dy/dt$. In the absence of any external forces, the resultant force acting on the mass is

$$\text{resultant force} = -ky - c\frac{dy}{dt}$$

Thus Newton's second law gives

$$m\frac{d^2y}{dt^2} = -ky - c\frac{dy}{dt}$$

and so

$$m\frac{d^2y}{dt^2} + c\frac{dy}{dt} + ky = 0 \qquad [13]$$

This homogeneous second-order differential equation describes the motion of a damped mechanical system.

If we have an external force $F(t)$ applied to the damped mechanical system then the differential equation becomes

$$m\frac{d^2y}{dt^2}+c\frac{dy}{dt}+ky=F(t) \qquad [14]$$

This non-homogeneous, second-order differential equation describes the forced oscillations of a mechanical system.

Example

Determine how the displacement y will vary with time t in seconds for a spring-mass mechanical system of mass 2 kg and spring stiffness 2 N/m when subject to an external force F with a rectangular waveform such that

$F(t) = 10$ for $0 \leq t < 1$
$F(t) = -10$ for $1 \leq t < 2$, period = 2 s

The waveform of the force can be described by the Fourier series (see table 2.1 item 2)

$$F=\frac{40}{\pi}\left(\sin \pi t+\frac{1}{3}\sin 3\pi t+\frac{1}{5}\sin 5\pi t+\ldots\right)$$

The differential equation describing the motion of the mass will be of the form given by equation [12] and thus

$$2\frac{d^2y}{dt^2}+2y=\frac{40}{\pi}\left(\sin \pi t+\frac{1}{3}\sin 3\pi t+\frac{1}{5}\sin 5\pi t+\ldots\right)$$

The corresponding homogeneous differential equation is

$$2\frac{d^2y}{dt^2}+2y=0$$

This gives an auxiliary equation of

$$2s^2+2=0$$

Thus $s = \sqrt{-1}$ and so $s = 0 + j1$. The solution of corresponding homogeneous differential equation is thus (see equation [6])

$$y_c = A\cos t + B\sin t$$

Considering just the first harmonic of the external force, then the particular integral that can be tried is

$$y_p = C\cos \pi t + D\sin \pi t$$

Using this in the differential equation gives

$$-2C\pi^2 \cos \pi t - 2D\pi^2 \sin \pi t + 2C \cos \pi t + 2D \sin \pi t$$

$$= \frac{40}{\pi} \sin \pi t$$

Equating the coefficients of the cosine terms gives $C = 0$. Equating the coefficients of the sine terms gives

$$-2D\pi^2 + 2D = \frac{40}{\pi}$$

Hence

$$y_p = \frac{20}{\pi(1 - \pi^2)}$$

For the third harmonic the particular integral is given by

$$y_p = C \cos 3\pi t + D \sin 3\pi t$$

Using this value in the differential equation gives

$$-18C\pi^2 \cos 3\pi t - 18D\pi^2 \sin 3\pi t + 2C \cos 3\pi t + 2D \sin 3\pi t$$

$$= \frac{40}{3\pi} \sin 3\pi t$$

Equating the coefficients of the cosine terms gives $C = 0$. Equating the coefficients of the sine terms gives

$$-18D\pi^2 + 2D = \frac{40}{3\pi}$$

Hence the particular integral is

$$y_p = \frac{20}{3\pi(1 - 9\pi^2)} \sin 3\pi t$$

For the fifth harmonic the particular integral is

$$y_p = C \cos 5\pi t + D \sin 5\pi t$$

Using this value in the differential equation gives

$$-50C\pi^2 \cos 5\pi t - 50D\pi^2 \sin 5\pi t + 2C \cos 5\pi t + 2D \sin 5\pi t$$

$$= \frac{40}{5\pi} \sin 5\pi t$$

Equating coefficients of cosine terms gives $C = 0$ and equating coefficients of the sine terms gives

$$-50D\pi^2 + 2D = \frac{40}{5\pi}$$

Thus the particular integral is

$$y_P = \frac{20}{5\pi(1-25\pi^2)} \sin 5\pi t$$

Hence we can write for the full solution for the differential equation

$$y = A \cos t + B \sin t + \frac{20}{\pi(1-\pi^2)} \sin \pi t + \frac{20}{3\pi(1-9\pi^2)} \sin 3\pi t$$

$$+ \frac{20}{5\pi(1-25\pi^2)} \sin 5\pi t + \ldots$$

Review problems

5 A mechanical system consists of a mass of 1 kg attached to a spring of stiffness 0.5 N/kg. How will the displacement of the mass vary with time when the following external forces F are applied along the line of the spring?

(a) $F(t) = \sin t$

(b) $F(t) = \sin t + \frac{1}{9} \sin 3t$

(c) $F(t) = t^2/4$ when $-\pi < t < \pi$, period $= 2\pi$

8.3.1 Selective resonance

With an undamped system subject to a sinusoidal forcing input, resonance is said to occur when the amplitude is infinite, this being when the forcing frequency equals the natural frequency of the system. With a damped system the amplitude is always finite, resonance occuring when the amplitude is a maximum. For a system subject to an external force which consists of a number of harmonics then resonance might occur at a harmonic. When this is the case then the amplitude of that harmonic is much magnified when compared with the other harmonics. The term *selective resonance* is used to describe this effect.

Review problems

6 A mass of 3 kg is suspended from a tethered spring of stiffness 27 N/kg. Determine how the displacement y of the mass will vary with time t when the external force F described by the following is applied along the line of the spring.

$$F(t) = -\pi t + t^2 \text{ for } -\pi < t < 0$$
$$F(t) = \pi t - t^2 \text{ for } 0 < t < \pi, \text{ period} = 2\pi$$

Further problems

7 Differentiate term-by-term the waveform function described by the following Fourier series. State whether the result is valid.

$$y = f(t) = 4.2 - 5.0 \cos t - 1.8 \cos 2t + 0.2 \cos 3t$$

8 Solve the following differential equations:

(a) $\dfrac{d^2y}{dt^2} + 16y = \sin t$

(b) $\dfrac{d^2y}{dt^2} + 16y = \sin t + \frac{1}{9}\sin 3t + \frac{1}{25}\sin 5t$

9 A spring-mass system has a mass of 1 kg and a spring stiffness of $\sqrt{2}$ N/kg. Determine how the displacement of the mass will vary with time when the system is subject to external forces along the line of the spring of:

(a) $F(t) = \sin t$

(b) $F(t) = \sin t + \frac{1}{9}\sin 3t + \frac{1}{25}\sin 5t$

10 A mass m is suspended from a spring of stiffness k. Determine how the displacement y of the mass will vary with time when an external force of $A \cos \omega t$ is applied along the line of the spring.

11 A spring-mass system has a mass of 1 kg and a spring of stiffness 10 N/kg. Determine how the displacement of the mass will vary with time when the system is subject to the following external force along the line of the spring. t is in seconds.

$$F(t) = 5t \text{ for } -2 < t < 2, \text{ period} = 4 \text{ s}$$

9 The Fourier transform

9.1 Non-periodic signals

In the preceding chapters the concern has been with periodic waveforms and their representation by Fourier series. In chapter 4 where non-periodic waveforms were considered in terms of the half-range sine and half-range cosine series, the technique used was to pretend they really were periodic. Thus the concern has only really been with periodic signals. In this chapter consideration is given to non-periodic, finite-duration, waveforms and how they can be represented. It may seem a contradiction to contemplate the representation of a non-periodic, finite-duration, waveform by sinusoids which are periodic and infinite in duration. The approach that is taken is to consider the non-periodic waveform as being what a periodic signal would become when the periodic time approaches infinity. Thus in the entire span of time we only see one cycle of the periodic waveform and this is what we term the non-periodic waveform.

A non-periodic, finite-duration, waveform is a signal which varies with time. The Fourier series represents a waveform in terms of angular frequencies, i.e. the harmonics. Thus the representation of a time varying signal is replaced by one which involves frequencies. This is the transformation that is carried out and is termed the *Fourier transform*. The term *inverse Fourier transform* is used for the reverse operation when a representation in terms of frequencies is transformed into a time-varying signal.

9.2 Fourier series to Fourier transform

Consider the periodic rectangular pulse train shown in figure 9.1 and its representation by means of the complex form of the Fourier series (see chapter 5 and in particular section 5.3.1). The amplitude V is a function of time. The complex coefficient c_n is given by (chapter 5 equation [9])

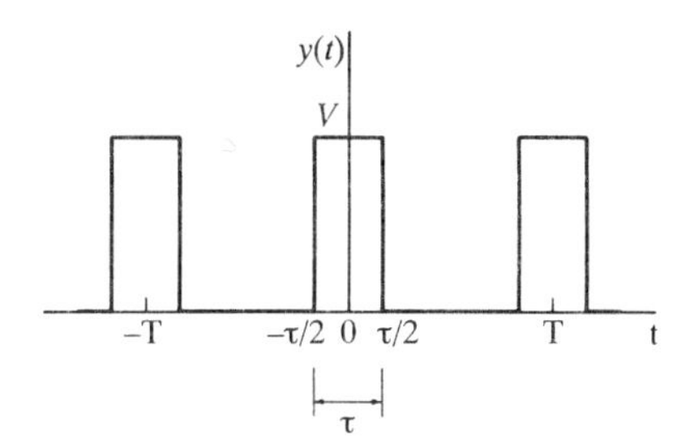

Fig. 9.1 Periodic pulse train

$$c_n = \frac{1}{T}\int_{-T/2}^{T/2} f(t)\,e^{-jn\omega_0 t}\,dt \qquad [1]$$

$$= \frac{1}{T}\int_{-\tau/2}^{\tau/2} V e^{-jn\omega_0 t}\,dt$$

$$= \frac{V}{T}\left[\frac{e^{-jn\omega_0 t}}{-jn\omega_0}\right]_{-\tau/2}^{\tau/2}$$

Since the frequency of the fundamental $\omega_0 = 2\pi/T$, then

$$c_n = -\frac{V}{j2n\pi}\left(e^{-jn\pi\tau/T} - e^{jn\pi\tau/T}\right)$$

Since $\sin\theta = (e^{j\theta} - e^{-j\theta})/2j$ then

$$c_n = \frac{V}{n\pi}\sin\frac{n\pi\tau}{T} \qquad [2]$$

This equation can be written in the form

$$c_n = \frac{V\tau}{T}\,\frac{\sin\dfrac{n\pi\tau}{T}}{\dfrac{n\pi\tau}{T}} \qquad [3]$$

We have a term in equation [3] of the form $(\sin x)/x$, with x being $n\pi\tau/T$. This factor is often referred to as sinc x and determines the shape of the amplitude spectrum of the harmonics, indicating how the amplitude is modified as n increases. Tables are available indicating the values of sinc x for various values of x. The value of sinc x is 1.0 at $x = 0$, decreasing to 0 at $x = 1.0$, negative between $x = 1.0$ and 2.0, 0 at $x = 2.0$, positive between $x = 2.0$ and 3.0, 0 at $x = 3.0$, etc.

Figure 9.2 shows the spectrum. We have a spectrum for which the amplitude is $V\tau/T$ when $n = 0$. When $n = 1$ we have a fundamental frequency of $\omega_0 = 2\pi/T$. When $n = 2$ the second harmonic frequency is $2 \times 2\pi/T$. When $n = 3$ the third harmonic

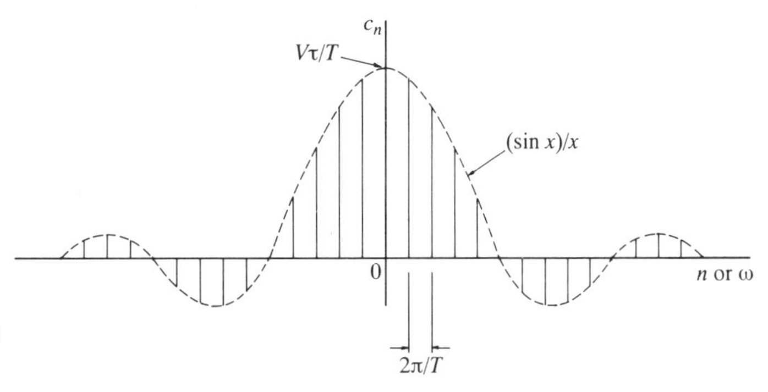

Fig. 9.2 Spectrum for the periodic pulse train

frequency is $3 \times 2\pi/T$. Thus the spacing between the frequency components is $\Delta\omega = 2\pi/T$. As the number n of the harmonic increases, i.e. as the angular frequency increases, from zero then the amplitude decreases by the factor $(\sin x)/x$. The amplitude will first become zero when

$$\sin\frac{n\pi\tau}{T} = 0$$

i.e. when $n = T/\tau$. This gives the number of harmonics up to the first zero amplitude value. The frequency of a harmonic is $n\omega_0$, i.e. $n2\pi/T$. Thus the frequency at which the amplitude first becomes zero is $(T/\tau)2\pi/T = 2\pi/\tau$.

with τ s staying the same

Now consider what happens to the pulse train and its spectrum when the periodic time T is increased. The general form of the shape of the amplitude spectrum will not change, still being given by $(\sin x)/x$. Due to the term $V\tau/T$ in equation [2], increasing T will result in a decrease in the amplitudes of every harmonic. Since the spacing $\Delta\omega$ between harmonics is $2\pi/T$ then the spacing between harmonics will decrease. The number of harmonics up to the first zero amplitude value will increase, since $n = T/\tau$. The frequency of this first zero amplitude will not change, since the frequency is $2\pi/\tau$. Figure 9.3 shows how the spectrum of the periodic pulse train is changed as the periodic time increases.

If the periodic time tends to an infinite value, i.e. $T \to \infty$, then we expect that the general form of the shape of the amplitude spectrum will not change and the amplitudes will be decreased at every harmonic. The spacing between the harmonics will decrease and the number of harmonics up to the first zero amplitude will

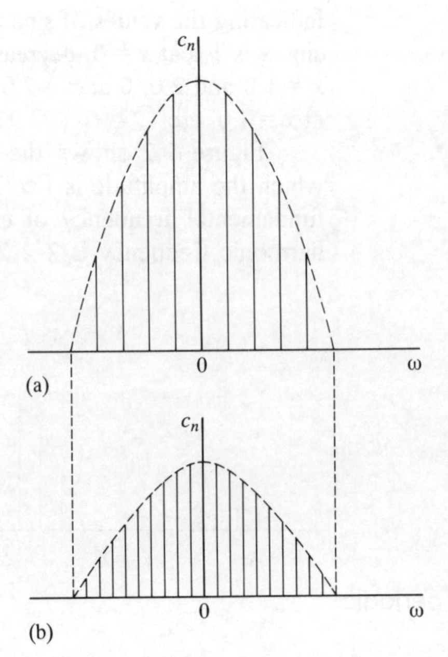

Fig. 9.3 Effect of increasing periodic time: (a) $T = 5\tau$, (b) $T = 10\tau$

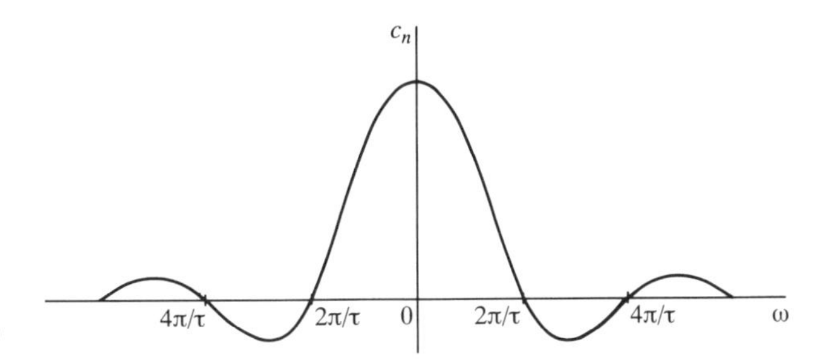

Fig. 9.4 The spectrum as $T \to \infty$

increase. This will result in so many harmonics that they will merge to give an amplitude graph which is a continuous function of frequency. Thus we now have a graph showing how the amplitude is distributed across the full range of frequency, as in figure 9.4. The frequencies of the first, and subsequent, zero amplitudes will not change.

Consider equation [1],

$$c_n = \frac{1}{T}\int_{-T/2}^{T/2} f(t)\,\mathrm{e}^{-\mathrm{j}n\omega_0 t}\,\mathrm{d}t$$

As $T \to \infty$ then $c_n \to 0$, i.e. the amplitudes at all frequencies tend to 0. However, if we write equation [1] in a different form we can end up with a quantity which does not tend to 0 as $T \to 0$.

$$c_n T \to \int_{-\infty}^{+\infty} f(t)\,\mathrm{e}^{-\mathrm{j}n\omega_0 t}\,\mathrm{d}t \text{ as } T \to \infty$$

As $T \to \infty$ then the spacing between harmonics $\Delta\omega$ becomes smaller and smaller and we can write it as $\Delta\omega \to \mathrm{d}\omega$. Since the amplitude spectrum becomes a continuous graph we can write, instead of the discrete harmonics, a continuously variable frequency ω, i.e. $n\omega_0 \to \omega$. Thus we can write the above equation as

$$c_n T \to \int_{-\infty}^{+\infty} f(t)\,\mathrm{e}^{-\mathrm{j}\omega t}\,\mathrm{d}t \text{ as } T \to \infty \qquad [4]$$

Since $c_n T = c_n 2\pi/\omega$ then the equation is giving a quantity which must be just a function of ω. If we represent this integral by some function $F(\omega)$ (note that this function is often written as $F(\mathrm{j}\omega)$ since the exponential term refers to $\mathrm{j}\omega$) then

$$c_n T \to F(\omega) \text{ as } T \to \infty \qquad [5]$$

with

$$F(\omega) = \int_{-\infty}^{+\infty} f(t)\,\mathrm{e}^{-\mathrm{j}\omega t}\,\mathrm{d}t \qquad [6]$$

This equation defines how a function of time $f(t)$ can be converted into a function of the angular frequency $F(\omega)$. $F(\omega)$ is said to be the *Fourier transform* of $f(t)$. This can be expressed as

$$F(\omega) = \mathcal{J}\{f(t)\} \qquad [7]$$

with the $\mathcal{J}$ indicating the Fourier transform operation.

In general, with the complex form of representation, the Fourier series is given by (chapter 5 equation [8])

$$f(t) = \sum_{n=-\infty}^{n=\infty} c_n \, e^{jn\omega_0 t}$$

Thus as $T \to \infty$ we have $n\omega_0 \to \omega$ and $c_n T \to F(\omega)$. Since we have $1/T = \omega_0/2\pi \to d\omega/2\pi$ then $c_n \to F(\omega)/T \to F(\omega)\, d\omega/2\pi$. With such small intervals $d\omega$, the discrete sum becomes a continuous sum and so the summation becomes an integral. The above equation then becomes

$$f(t) = \frac{1}{2\pi}\int_{-\infty}^{+\infty} F(\omega)\, e^{j\omega t}\, d\omega \qquad [8]$$

This equation defines how a function of angular frequency $F(\omega)$ can be converted into a function of time $f(t)$. It thus is the *inverse Fourier transform* of $F(\omega)$. This can be written as

$$f(t) = \mathcal{J}^{-1}\{F(\omega)\} \qquad [9]$$

Equations [6] and [8] are together called the *Fourier transform pair*, since one describes how a function of time can be transformed into a function of angular frequency and the other how a function of angular frequency can be transformed into a function of time. The Fourier transform can be said to enable non-periodic functions of time to be described by functions of frequency, i.e. functions in the *time domain* are transformed into functions in the *frequency domain*.

9.2.1 The Fourier transform

The Fourier transform of a function $f(t)$ is defined by equation [6] as

$$\mathcal{J}\{f(t)\} = F(\omega) = \int_{-\infty}^{+\infty} f(t)\, e^{-j\omega t}\, dt$$

The transform is, in general, a *complex quantity*. The exponential term can be written in terms of cosines and sines to give

$$F(\omega) = \int_{-\infty}^{+\infty} f(t)\,(\cos\omega t - \mathrm{j}\sin\omega t)\,\mathrm{d}t$$

$$= \int_{-\infty}^{+\infty} f(t)\,\cos\omega t\,\mathrm{d}t - \mathrm{j}\int_{-\infty}^{+\infty} f(t)\,\sin\omega t\,\mathrm{d}t$$

The transform is thus the sum of a real term: the first integral; and an imaginary term: the second integral. If we simplify this equation by writing

$$A(\omega) = \int_{-\infty}^{+\infty} f(t)\,\cos\omega t\,\mathrm{d}t$$

and

$$B(\omega) = \int_{-\infty}^{+\infty} f(t)\,\sin\omega t\,\mathrm{d}t$$

then

$$F(\omega) = A(\omega) - \mathrm{j}B(\omega)$$

The magnitude of $F(\omega)$, i.e. $|F(\omega)|$, is thus

$$|F(\omega)| = \sqrt{A^2(\omega) + B^2(\omega)} \qquad [10]$$

and the phase $\phi(\omega)$ is

$$\phi(\omega) = \tan^{-1}\frac{-B(\omega)}{A(\omega)} \qquad [11]$$

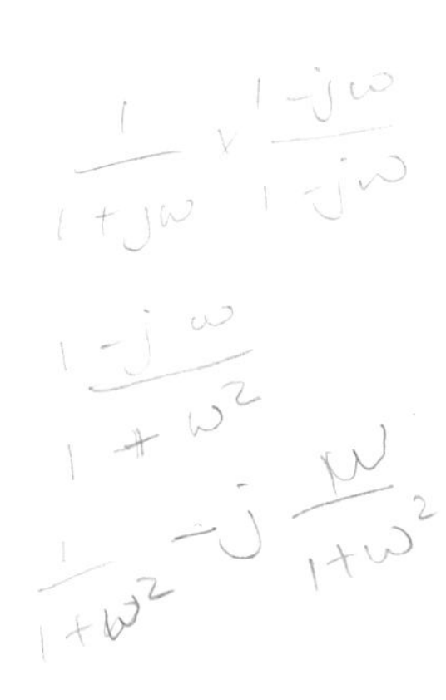

Example

Determine the magnitude and the phase of the Fourier transform $1/(1 + \mathrm{j}\omega)$.

The transform can be rearranged in the form $A(\omega) + \mathrm{j}B(\omega)$.

$$\frac{1}{1+\mathrm{j}\omega} = \frac{1}{1+\mathrm{j}\omega} \times \frac{1-\mathrm{j}\omega}{1-\mathrm{j}\omega} = \frac{1-\mathrm{j}\omega}{1+\omega^2}$$

Thus $A = 1/(1 + \omega^2)$ and $B = -\,\omega/(1 + \omega^2)$. Hence

$$|F(\omega)| = \sqrt{\left(\frac{1}{1+\omega^2}\right)^2 + \left(\frac{-\omega}{1+\omega^2}\right)^2}$$

$$= \frac{1}{\sqrt{1+\omega^2}}$$

The phase is

$$\phi(\omega) = \tan^{-1}\left(\frac{\omega}{1}\right)$$

Review problems

1 Determine the magnitudes and phases of the following Fourier transforms:
(a) 1, (b) 2/jω, (c) 1/(2 + jω)

9.3 Fourier transforms

Consider the rectangular pulse of duration τ illustrated in figure 9.5. The Fourier transform can be found by means of equation [6].

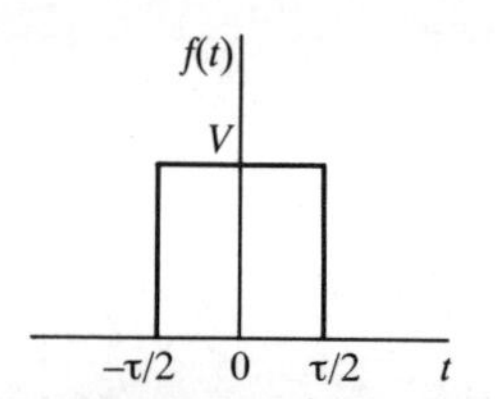

Fig. 9.5 Rectangular pulse

$$F(\omega) = \int_{-\infty}^{+\infty} f(t)\, e^{-j\omega t}\, dt$$

$$= \int_{-\tau/2}^{\tau/2} V e^{-j\omega t}\, d\omega$$

$$= \left[\frac{V e^{-j\omega t}}{-j\omega}\right]_{-\tau/2}^{\tau/2}$$

$$= \frac{V}{-j\omega}(e^{-j\omega\tau/2} - e^{j\omega\tau/2})$$

$$= \frac{2V}{\omega} \sin \frac{\omega\tau}{2}$$

This can be expressed as

$$F(\omega) = V\tau \frac{\sin \omega\tau/2}{\omega\tau/2} \qquad [12]$$

This is the Fourier transform of the rectangular pulse. The term $(\sin x)/x$ is often called sinc x. Thus equation [12] can be written as $F(\omega) = V\tau \operatorname{sinc}(\omega\tau/2)$.

Compare this with the equation for a periodic train of rectangular pulses (equation [3])

$$c_n = \frac{V\tau}{T}\frac{\sin \dfrac{n\pi\tau}{T}}{\dfrac{n\pi\tau}{T}} = \frac{V\tau}{T}\frac{\sin n\omega_0\tau/2}{n\omega_0\tau/2}$$

where ω_0 is the fundamental angular frequency. A graph, for the single pulse, of $F(\omega)$ against ω (figure 9.6) has the same shape as the amplitude envelope in the graph for the periodic train of pulses

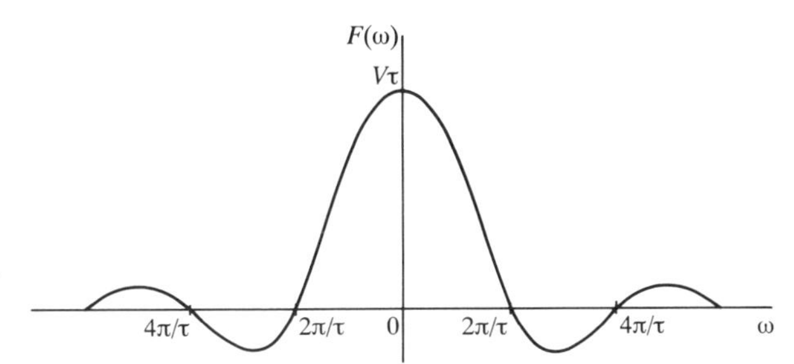

Fig. 9.6 The Fourier transform of a pulse

of c_n against $n\omega_0$. The amplitude spectrum has altered from a discrete line spectrum to a continuous spectrum. Thus we have a physical interpretation of the Fourier transform $F(\omega)$ as being a measure of the frequency content of $f(t)$.

Consider the significance of equation [12] and its graph, figure 9.6, with regard to such a signal being the input to an electronic system. Most of the spectrum can be considered to fall within the central maximum of the graph. This means angular frequencies up to $2\pi/\tau$. This is a frequency limit of $f = \omega/2\pi = 1/\tau$ and so an electronic system that passes frequencies up to $1/\tau$ will give little distortion of the pulse. The narrower the pulse the smaller τ and so the greater the bandwidth required of the system if distortion is to be kept low.

Example

Determine the Fourier transform for a signal for which

$$f(t) = e^{-at} \text{ for } 0 \leq t$$
$$f(t) = 0 \text{ for } t < 0$$

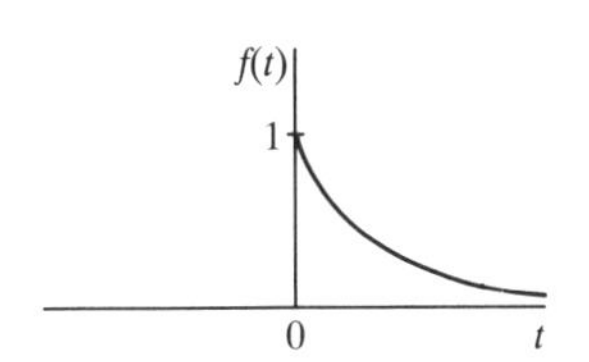

Fig. 9.7 Example

Figure 9.7 shows the signal. Hence the Fourier transform is given by equation [6] as

$$F(\omega) = \int_{-\infty}^{+\infty} f(t)\, e^{-j\omega t}\, dt = \int_{0}^{+\infty} e^{-at}\, e^{-j\omega t}\, dt$$

$$= \int_{0}^{+\infty} e^{-(a+j\omega)t}\, dt$$

$$= \frac{1}{-(a+j\omega)}\left[e^{-(a+j\omega)t}\right]_0^{\infty}$$

$$= \frac{1}{a+j\omega} \qquad [13]$$

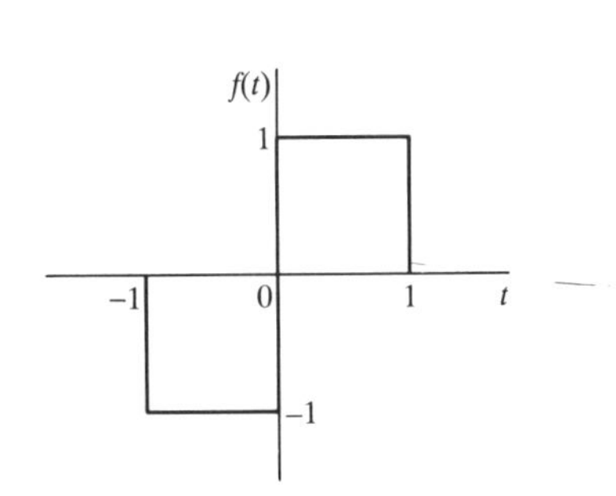

Fig. 9.8 Problem 2

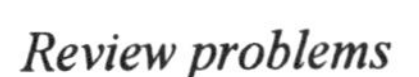

Review problems

2 Determine the Fourier transforms for (a) the signal shown in figure 9.8, (b) the signal for which

$$f(t) = e^{-at} \text{ for } 0 < t$$
$$f(t) = e^{at} \text{ for } t < 0$$

9.3.1 The impulse function

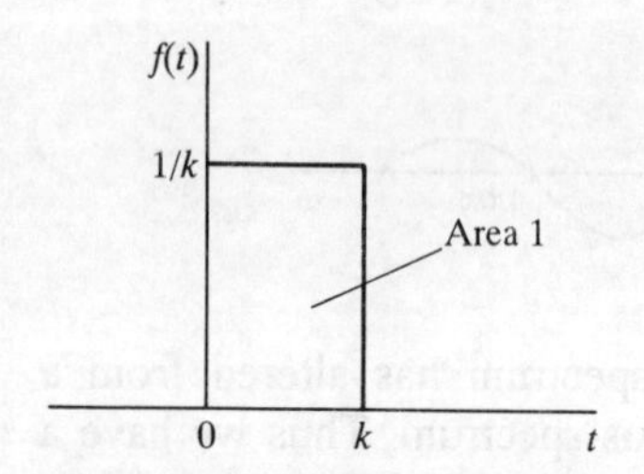

Fig. 9.9 Pulse with area 1

Consider a rectangular pulse of size $1/k$ that occurs at time $t = 0$ and which has a pulse width of k, i.e. the area of the pulse is 1. Figure 9.9 shows such a pulse. The pulse can be described as

$$f(t) = 1/k \text{ for } 0 \leq t < k$$
$$f(t) = 0 \text{ for } t > k$$

If we maintain this constant pulse area of 1 then decreasing the width of the pulse, i.e. reducing k, increases the height. In the limit as $k \to 0$ then we end up with just a vertical line at $t = 0$, the height of the line going off to infinity. Such a graph can be used to represent an impulse. The impulse is said to be a unit impulse because the area enclosed by it is 1. This function is represented by $\delta(t)$, being called the *unit-impulse function* or the *Dirac-delta function.*

The Fourier transform for the impulse function is thus given by equation [6] as

$$\mathcal{F}\{\delta(t)\} = \int_{-\infty}^{\infty} \delta(t)\, e^{-j\omega t}\, dt$$

Since the impulse function has a zero value over all time, except at $t = 0$, the limits for the exponential need not be written out to infinity but as 0+ and 0−. This indicates that we are summing to just either side of the 0. Thus

$$\mathcal{F}\{\delta(t)\} = \int_{0-}^{0+} \delta(t)\, e^{-j\omega t}\, dt$$

If a unit-impulse is multiplied by a function of time then the strength of that function must be the value of that function at the time of the impulse. This is because at all other times the impulse strength is zero and we are multiplying by zero. The value of the exponential function in the above integral at $t = 0$ is 1. Thus the integral can be written as

$$\mathcal{F}\{\delta(t)\} = \int_{0-}^{0+} \delta(t) 1\, dt$$

However, the integral of $\delta(t)$ over time is the area under the impulse function, i.e. 1. Thus

$$\mathcal{F}\{\delta(t)\} = 1 \qquad [14]$$

The Fourier transform tells us that the impulse function contains all frequencies, the magnitude of the transform $|F(\omega)|$ being 1 for all values of ω. This is what would be expected from the earlier discussion (section 9.3) of the rectangular pulse and how its frequency spectrum changes as the width of the pulse is reduced; an impulse just being a rectangular pulse which has been reduced to the limit.

9.3.2 A constant

Consider the determination of the Fourier transform of a constant, i.e. $f(t) = A$. If we substitute this into equation [6] we end up with

$$\int_{-\infty}^{+\infty} f(t)\,e^{-j\omega t}\,dt = \int_{-\infty}^{+\infty} A\,e^{-j\omega t}\,dt = A\left[\frac{e^{-j\omega t}}{-j\omega}\right]_{-\infty}^{+\infty}$$

which is an indeterminate expression. This is because the function being integrated does not converge, i.e. the area under the function does not have a finite value but tends to infinity. This also applies if we try to obtain, by directly using equation [6], the Fourier transform for a sinusoidal function or a step function.

To obtain the Fourier transform for a constant we have to adopt a subterfuge. We consider a function which does converge and which, if we consider a limiting value of it, does approximate to a constant. Such a function is the exponential function $A\,e^{-at}$ with $a > 0$ and spreading out both towards $+\infty$ and $-\infty$. As $a \to 0$ then the exponential function $f(t) \to A$. Figure 9.10 illustrates this.

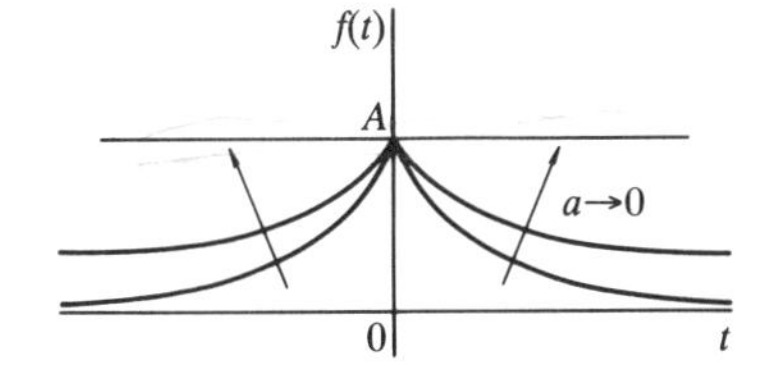

Fig. 9.10 The approximation of a constant by an exponential function

The Fourier transform for the exponential with $|t|$ is

$$F(\omega) = \int_{-\infty}^{+\infty} A\,e^{-at}\,e^{-j\omega t}\,dt$$

$$= \int_{-\infty}^{0} A\,e^{at}\,e^{-j\omega t}\,dt + \int_{0}^{+\infty} A\,e^{-at}\,e^{-j\omega t}\,dt$$

$$= \frac{A}{a - j\omega}\left[e^{(a-j\omega)t}\right]_{-\infty}^{0} + \frac{A}{-(a+j\omega)}\left[e^{-(a+j\omega)t}\right]_{0}^{+\infty}$$

$$= \frac{A}{a - j\omega} + \frac{A}{a + j\omega}$$

$$= \frac{2Aa}{a^2 + \omega^2} \qquad [15]$$

With $\omega = 0$ then we have $F(\omega) = 2A/a$. Then as $a \to 0$ we have $F(\omega) \to \infty$. This is also what we obtain with an impulse function. Thus the Fourier transform is an impulse. The area under the $F(\omega)$ graph against ω is the strength of the impulse. Thus the strength is

$$\int_{-\infty}^{+\infty} \frac{2Aa}{a^2+\omega^2}\,d\omega = 4aA\int_0^{+\infty} \frac{1}{a^2+\omega^2}\,d\omega$$

$$= 4aA\left[\frac{1}{a}\tan^{-1}\frac{\omega}{a}\right]_0^{+\infty}$$

$$= 4A\left(\frac{\pi}{2} - 0\right)$$

$$= 2\pi A$$

Hence the Fourier transform of the constant is an impulse of strength $2\pi A$, i.e.

$$\mathcal{F}\{A\} = 2\pi A\,\delta(\omega) \qquad [16]$$

This tells us that the frequency spectrum of a constant signal consists of a single frequency line of amplitude $2\pi A$ at a frequency of $\omega = 0$.

Review problems

3 Determine the Fourier transform of the function described by

$f(t) = -1$ for $0 < t$
$f(t) = +1$ for $t > 0$

Figure 9.11 shows a graph of the function and a hint as to how the function can be considered as the limits of exponential functions. This function is often referred to as the *signum function* and written as sgn (t).

9.3.3 Standard Fourier transforms

Tables 9.1 gives the Fourier transforms for commonly encountered functions.

The function used to describe a unit step is $u(t)$. The unit-step function $u(t)$ indicates that the unit step starts at $t = 0$ and has the value 1 for a positive values of time, i.e.

$f(t) = 1$ for $0 \le t < \infty$
$f(t) = 0$ for $-\infty \le t < 0$

The unit-step function $u(-t)$ indicates a step which has the value 0 for all positive times greater than 0 and the value 1 for all times less than 0, i.e. negative times.

$f(t) = 1$ for $0 \le t < \infty$
$f(t) = 0$ for $-\infty \le t < 0$

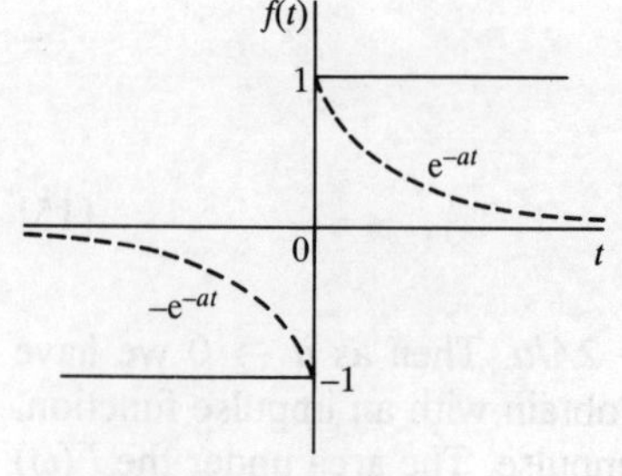

Fig. 9.11 Problem 3

Table 9.1 Fourier transforms

	$f(t)$ graphically	$f(t)$	$\mathcal{F}\{f(t)\}$	$\lvert F(\omega)\rvert$ spectrum
1	Impulse	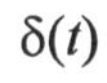 $\delta(t)$	1	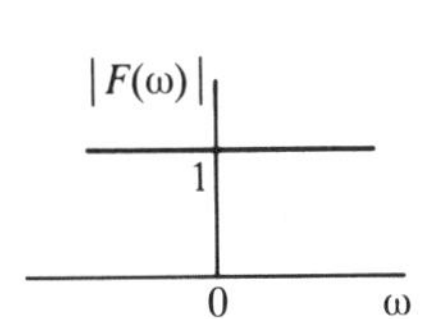
2	Constant 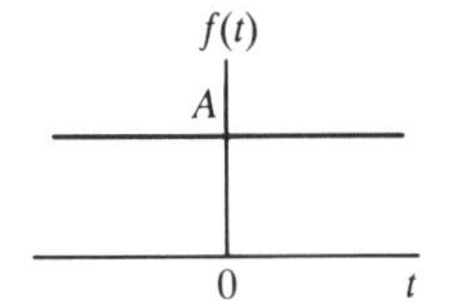	A	$2A\pi\delta(\omega)$	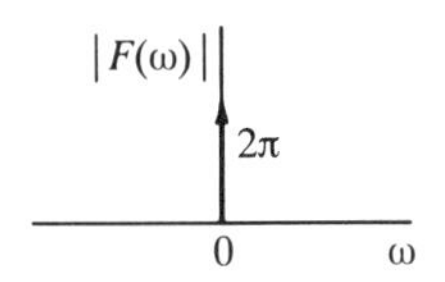
3	Unit step 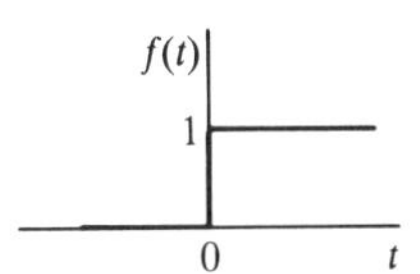	$u(t)$	$\pi\delta(\omega)+\frac{1}{j\omega}$	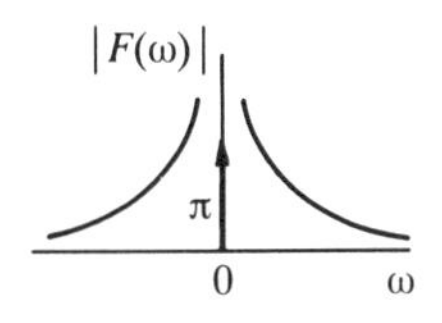
4	Signum function	$\text{sgn}(t) = u(t) - u(-t)$	$\frac{2}{j\omega}$	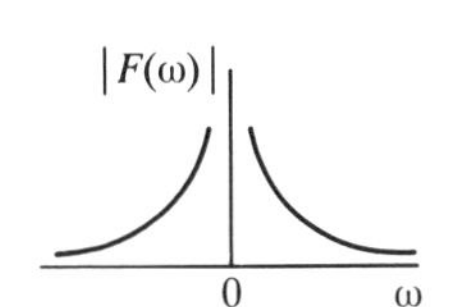
5	Pulse 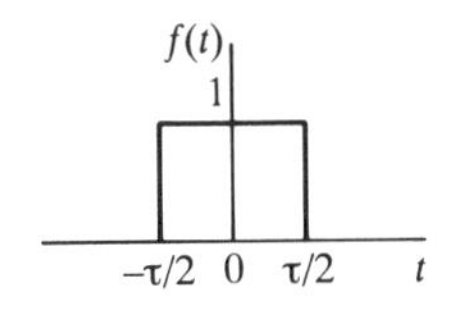	$u(t+\tau/2) - u(t-\tau/2)$	$\tau\frac{\sin\omega\tau/2}{\omega\tau/2}$	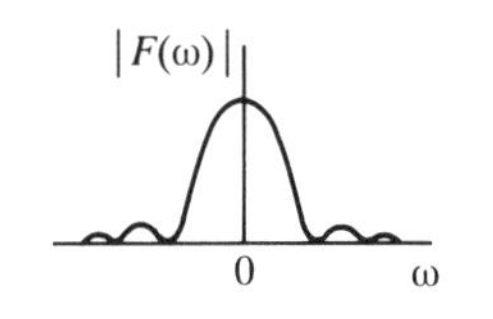
6	Positive time exponential 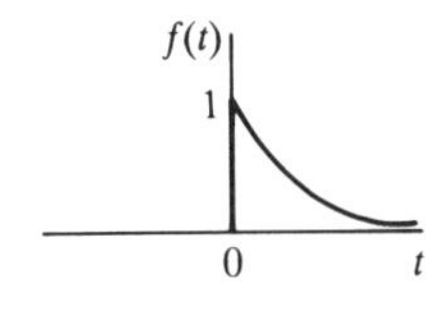	$e^{-at}\,u(t)$	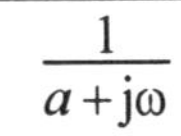 $\frac{1}{a+j\omega}$	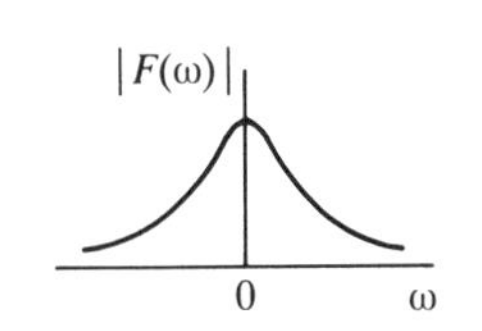

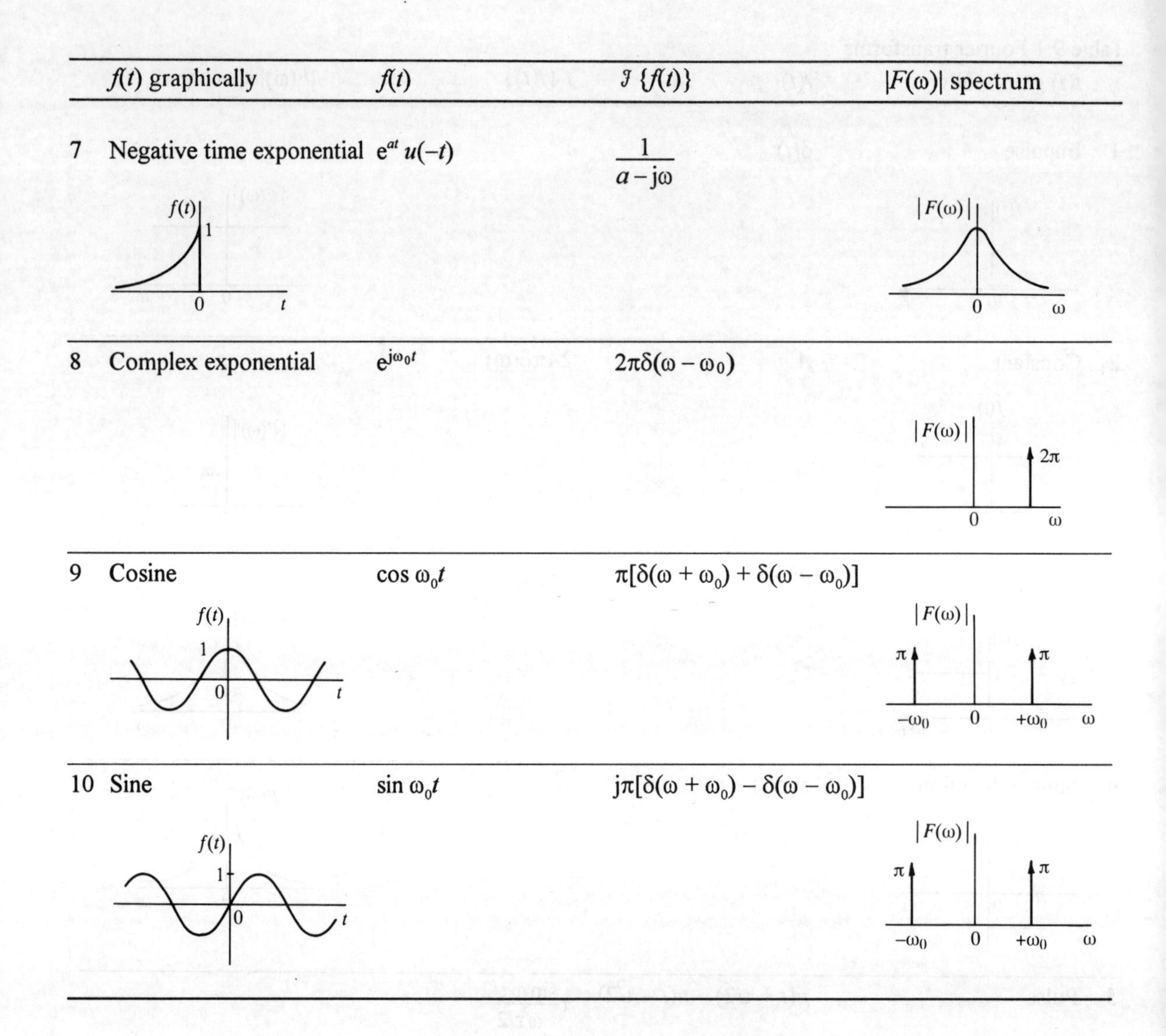

	$f(t)$ graphically	$f(t)$	$\mathcal{F}\{f(t)\}$	$\lvert F(\omega)\rvert$ spectrum
7	Negative time exponential	$e^{at}\, u(-t)$	$\dfrac{1}{a - j\omega}$	
8	Complex exponential	$e^{j\omega_0 t}$	$2\pi\delta(\omega - \omega_0)$	
9	Cosine	$\cos \omega_0 t$	$\pi[\delta(\omega + \omega_0) + \delta(\omega - \omega_0)]$	
10	Sine	$\sin \omega_0 t$	$j\pi[\delta(\omega + \omega_0) - \delta(\omega - \omega_0)]$	

The step function is often combined with other functions in the form $f(t)u(t)$. This indicates that at times before $t = 0$ the function is multiplied by 0 and at positive times greater than 0 it is multiplied by 1. Thus $e^{-at}u(t)$ is an exponential function which at $t = 0$ has the value of the step function, namely 1, and increases in a positive time direction. The function $e^{-at}u(-t)$ is an exponential function which has the value 1 at $t = 0$ and increases in a negative time direction.

The function $u(t - \tau)$ indicates that the unit step starts at $+\tau$, this being the value of time for which the function has a zero value. Thus the pulse function, item 5 in Table 9.1, can be considered to be the sum of two unit step functions, one with a positive step at $-\tau/2$ plus one with a negative step at $\tau/2$. Likewise, the impulse function $\delta(t)$ indicates a function which occurs at $t = 0$, while $\delta(t - \tau)$ indicates an impulse function which occurs at time τ.

Review problems

4 Use table 9.1 to obtain the Fourier transforms of the following functions:
(a) a unit step, (b) $e^{j\omega_0 t}$, (c) $\cos \omega_0 t$.

9.4 Properties of the Fourier transform

The following are discussions of some of the basic properties of Fourier transforms.

9.4.1 Linearity

Suppose that $f(t) = f_1(t) + f_2(t)$. Then

$$\mathcal{F}\{f_1(t) + f_2(t)\} = \int_{-\infty}^{+\infty} \{f_1(t) + f_2(t)\} e^{-j\omega t}\, dt$$

$$= \int_{-\infty}^{+\infty} f_1(t)\, e^{-j\omega t}\, dt + \int_{-\infty}^{+\infty} f_2(t)\, e^{-j\omega t}\, dt$$

$$= \mathcal{F}\{f_1(t)\} + \mathcal{F}\{f_2(t)\} \qquad [17]$$

Thus the Fourier transform of a sum of two functions is the sum of the Fourier transforms of each functions, considered separately. Due to this, the Fourier transform is said to be *linear*.

Example

Derive the Fourier transform for the function $\cos \omega_0 t$.

The function can be expressed as

$$\cos \omega_0 t = \frac{e^{j\omega_0 t} + e^{-j\omega_0 t}}{2}$$

Thus

$$\mathcal{F}\{\cos \omega_0 t\} = \tfrac{1}{2}(\mathcal{F}\{e^{j\omega_0 t}\} + \mathcal{F}\{e^{-j\omega_0 t}\})$$

$$= \tfrac{1}{2}[2\pi\delta(\omega - \omega_0) + 2\pi\delta(\omega + \omega_0)]$$

$$= \pi\delta(\omega - \omega_0) + \pi\delta(\omega + \omega_0) \qquad [18]$$

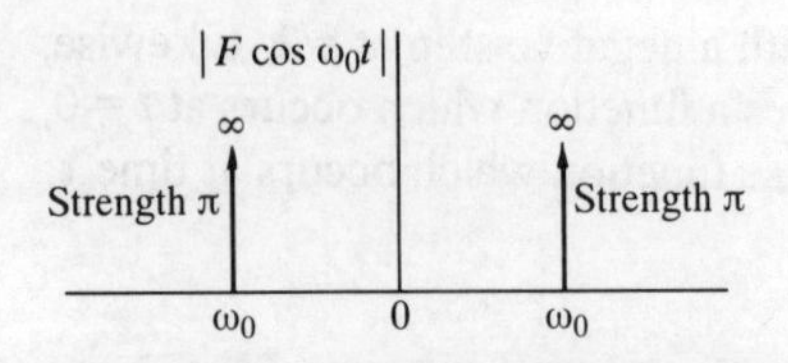

Fig. 9.12 Amplitude spectrum of $\cos \omega_0 t$

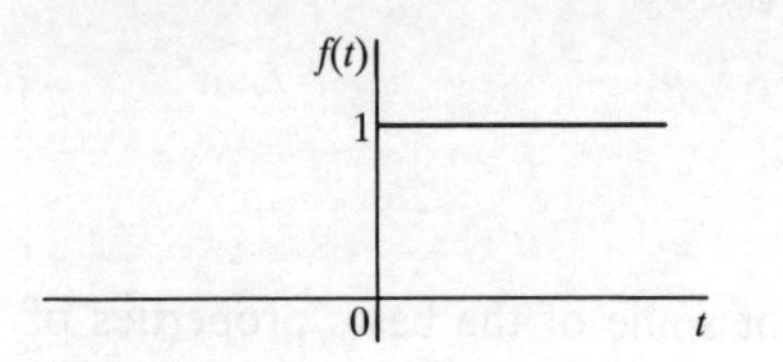

Fig. 9.13 Problem 5

The $\cos \omega_0 t$ function thus has an amplitude spectrum consisting of two lines, one at $-\omega_0$ and the other at $+\omega_0$. Each line is an impulse of strength π. Figure 9.12 shows the spectrum.

Review problems

5 Determine the Fourier transform of the function shown in figure 9.13. This function is called a *unit-step function*. Hint: use the linearity property and consider the unit step to be made up of two functions: a constant signal of 1/2 and the function described by figure 9.11 (problem 3) with amplitudes of +1/2 and −1/2.

9.4.2 Multiplication by a constant

Consider the effect on the Fourier transform of multiplying a function by a constant K.

$$\mathcal{F}\{Kf(t)\} = \int_{-\infty}^{+\infty} Kf(t)\,\mathrm{e}^{-\mathrm{j}\omega t}\,\mathrm{d}t = K\int_{-\infty}^{+\infty} f(t)\,\mathrm{e}^{-\mathrm{j}\omega t}\,\mathrm{d}t$$

Thus, if $\mathcal{F}\{f(t)\} = F(\omega)$,

$$\mathcal{F}\{Kf(t)\} = KF(\omega) \qquad [19]$$

Example

Determine the Fourier transform of an impulse of strength 2π, i.e. $2\pi\,\delta(t)$.

The Fourier transform of a unit-strength impulse is 1. Thus, using equation [19],

$$\mathcal{F}\{2\pi\,\delta(t)\} = 2\pi F(\omega) = 2\pi \times 1 = 2\pi$$

9.4.3 Even and odd symmetries

The Fourier transform can be expressed in terms of sines and cosines. Thus

$$F(\omega) = \int_{-\infty}^{+\infty} f(t)\,\mathrm{e}^{-\mathrm{j}\omega t}\,\mathrm{d}t$$

$$= \int_{-\infty}^{+\infty} f(t)[\cos\omega t - \mathrm{j}\sin\omega t]\,\mathrm{d}t$$

$$= \int_{-\infty}^{+\infty} f(t)\cos\omega t\,\mathrm{d}t - \int_{-\infty}^{+\infty} f(t)\,\mathrm{j}\sin\omega t\,\mathrm{d}t \qquad [20]$$

For an even function $f(t) = f(-t)$ then we have the product of an even function and an odd function, the sin ωt, in the second integral. The result is the integral of an odd function and so the second integral has a zero value (see section 3.2). Thus, for an even function, $F(\omega)$ is real.

For an odd function $f(t) = -f(-t)$ then we have the product of an odd function and an even function, the cos ωt, in the first integral. The result is the integral of an odd function and so the first integral has a zero value. Thus, for an odd function, $F(\omega)$ is imaginary.

Example

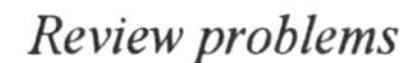

Fig. 9.14 Example

For the waveform described by figure 9.14, will the Fourier transform be real or imaginary?

The waveform is even and thus the Fourier transform will be real.

Review problems

6 For the waveforms described by figure 9.15, will the Fourier transforms be real or imaginary?

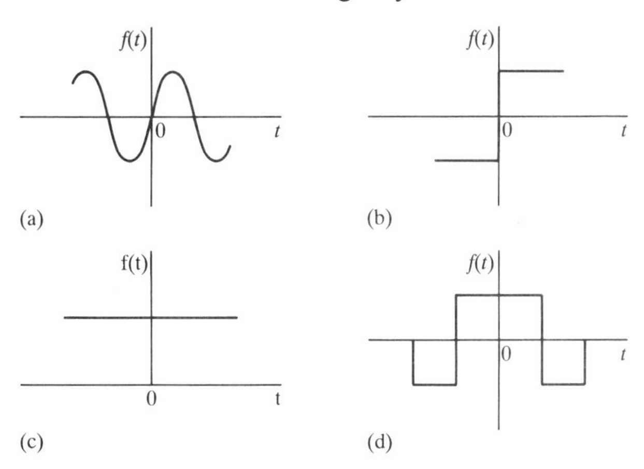

Fig. 9.15 Problem 6

9.4.4 Time scaling

Consider what happens to the Fourier transform for a pulse when the width of the pulse is changed. The Fourier transform for a function of time $f(at)$, where a is a real constant, is given by

$$\mathcal{F}\{f(at)\} = \int_{-\infty}^{+\infty} f(at)\, e^{-j\omega t}\, dt$$

If we let $x = at$ then $t = x/a$ and $dt = dx/a$. Thus

$$\mathcal{F}\{f(at)\} = \frac{1}{a}\int_{-\infty}^{+\infty} f(x) e^{-j(\omega/a)x}\, dx$$

The integral is what we would obtain for the Fourier transform of $f(t)$ if we just replaced ω by ω/a. Thus, if $\mathcal{F}\{f(t)\} = F(\omega)$, then

$$\mathcal{F}\{f(at)\} = \frac{1}{|a|}F\left(\frac{\omega}{a}\right) \quad [21]$$

Thus reducing the time over which a pulse exists, i.e. reducing a, increases the range of frequencies. An impulse, which is the shortest duration pulse, has a spectrum extending from $\omega = +\infty$ to $-\infty$. A constant d.c. signal is effectively an infinite duration pulse and has a spectrum consisting of just a single frequency.

Example

If the Fourier transform of a pulse of width 1 is sinc $\omega/2$, what will be the transform of a pulse of width 2?

A width of 2 means that the time scale in $f(t)$ is replaced by $f(t/2)$, i.e. $a = 1/2$. The Fourier transform of the width 2 pulse is thus 2 sinc ω. Since sinc $x = (\sin x)/x$ then 2 sinc ω is $(2 \sin \omega)/\omega$.

9.4.5 Time reversal

The time scaling property discussed above gives, when $a = -1$ in equation [21],

$$\mathcal{F}\{f(-t)\} = F(-\omega) \quad [22]$$

Thus the Fourier transform of a function with negative times is just the Fourier transform of $f(t)$ with negative frequencies. See, for example, items 6 and 7 in table 9.1.

9.4.6 Time shifting

Consider what happens when a signal is delayed by some time t_0.

$$\mathcal{F}\{f(t - t_0)\} = \int_{-\infty}^{+\infty} f(t - t_0)\, e^{-j\omega t}\, dt$$

$$= e^{-j\omega t_0} \int_{-\infty}^{+\infty} f(t - t_0)\, e^{-j\omega(t - t_0)}\, dt$$

However, the integral is just the Fourier transform we would obtain for $f(t)$ if we changed the time scale by a time t_0. Therefore, this is the same as the Fourier transform of $f(t)$. Thus

$$\mathcal{F}\{f(t - t_0)\} = e^{-j\omega t_0} F(\omega) \quad [23]$$

where $F(\omega)$ is the Fourier transform of $f(t)$.

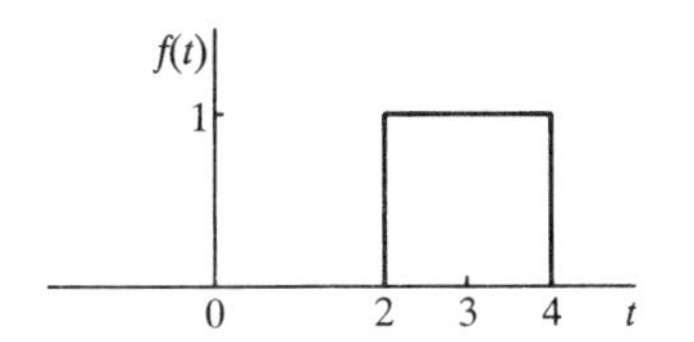

Fig. 9.16 Example

Example

Determine the Fourier transform of the delayed rectangular pulse shown in figure 9.16.

The Fourier transform for a pulse centred on $t = 0$ is given by item 5 in table 9.1 as

$$F(\omega) = \tau \frac{\sin \omega\tau/2}{\omega\tau/2}$$

where τ is the pulse width. Since $\tau = 2$ then such a pulse has the transform

$$F(\omega) = \frac{2 \sin \omega}{\omega}$$

The pulse is delayed by a time of 3. Thus the Fourier transform of the delayed pulse is

$$e^{-j3\omega} \frac{2 \sin \omega}{\omega}$$

Review problems

7 Determine the Fourier transform of the positive time exponential function e^{-t} which is delayed by a time of 4, i.e. $e^{-(t-4)}\, u(t-4)$.

9.4.7 Frequency shifting

Consider the Fourier transform of a product of $e^{j\omega_0 t}$ and a function of time $f(t)$, where ω_0 is some fixed value of angular frequency.

$$\mathcal{F}\{e^{j\omega_0 t} f(t)\} = e^{j\omega_0 t} \int_{-\infty}^{+\infty} f(t)\, e^{-j\omega t}\, dt$$

$$= \int_{-\infty}^{+\infty} f(t)\, e^{-j(\omega - \omega_0)t}\, dt$$

However, this is just the Fourier transform $F(\omega)$ when it has a frequency shift of ω_0. Thus

$$\mathcal{F}\{e^{j\omega_0 t} f(t)\} = F(\omega - \omega_0) \qquad [24]$$

Example

Determine the Fourier transform of $e^{-jt} f(t)$ where

$$\mathcal{F}\{f(t)\} = (2 \sin \omega)/\omega$$

If we multiply a function by e^{-jt} then the Fourier transform of that function is frequency shifted by −1. Hence the transform of the shifted function is

$$\frac{2\sin(\omega+1)}{\omega+1}$$

Review problems

8 Determine the Fourier transform of the following function

$$f(t) = 1\ e^{j3} \text{ for } |t| \le 1$$
$$f(t) = 0 \text{ for } |t| > 1$$

given that the Fourier transform of

$$f(t) = 1 \text{ for } |t| \le 1$$
$$f(t) = 0 \text{ for } |t| > 1$$

is $(2 \sin \omega)/\omega$.

9.4.8 Symmetry

The Fourier transform of a unit-strength impulse is 1, i.e. a constant over all values of ω (see item 1 in table 9.1.), i.e.

$$\mathcal{F}\{\delta(t)\} = 1$$

The Fourier transform of a constant input of 1 is an impulse of strength 2π (see item 2 in table 9.1), i.e.

$$\mathcal{F}\{1\} = 2\pi\ \delta(\omega)$$

There is a form of symmetry here in that the Fourier transform of an impulse is a constant and the Fourier transform of a constant is an impulse.

In general, if $\mathcal{F}\{f(t)\} = F(\omega)$ then equation [8] gives

$$f(t) = \frac{1}{2\pi}\int_{-\infty}^{+\infty} F(\omega)\,e^{j\omega t}\,d\omega$$

Thus

$$2\pi f(t) = \int_{-\infty}^{+\infty} F(\omega)\,e^{j\omega t}\,d\omega \qquad [25]$$

Equation [6] gives

$$F(\omega) = \int_{-\infty}^{+\infty} f(t)\,e^{-j\omega t}\,dt$$

and if we write this equation for $-\omega$ then

$$F(-\omega) = \int_{-\infty}^{+\infty} f(t)\, e^{j\omega t}\, dt \qquad [26]$$

The integrals in equations [25] and [26] are interchangeable if $f(t)$ and $F(\omega)$ are interchanged. The only difference between the expressions when such an interchange occurs is the 2π factor.

A unit height pulse of duration τ (item 5 in table 9.1) gives a Fourier transform of $\tau \sin(\omega\tau/2)/(\omega\tau/2)$. Conversely, a function of time signal of $\tau \sin(\omega\tau/2)/(\omega\tau/2)$ gives a Fourier transform which is a pulse waveform of height 2π.

9.4.9 Amplitude modulation

Amplitude modulation involves the amplitude of one signal being used to control the amplitude of a sinusoidal carrier. If the sinusoidal carrier is represented by $\cos \omega_c t$ and the controlling function by $f(t)$ then the amplitude modulated signal varies with time according to $f(t) \cos \omega_c t$. The Fourier transform of this signal can be written, when the cosine is written in exponential form, as

$$\mathcal{F}\{f(t) \cos \omega_c t\} = \mathcal{F}\{f(t)\, \tfrac{1}{2}(e^{j\omega_c t} + e^{-j\omega_c t})\}$$

Using the frequency-shifting property (equation [24]) then

$$\mathcal{F}\{f(t) \cos \omega_c t\} = \mathcal{F}\{\tfrac{1}{2} e^{j\omega_c t} f(t)\} + \mathcal{F}\{\tfrac{1}{2} e^{-j\omega_c t} f(t)\}$$

Thus if $\mathcal{F}\{f(t)\} = F(\omega)$ then

$$\mathcal{F}\{f(t) \cos \omega_c t\} = \tfrac{1}{2}F(\omega - \omega_c) + \tfrac{1}{2}F(\omega + \omega_c) \qquad [27]$$

The modulating process has thus centred the signal spectrum of $f(t)$ on the frequencies of $+\omega_c$ and $-\omega_c$.

9.5 Derivatives

A function $f(t)$ has a Fourier transform of

$$\mathcal{F}\{f(t)\} = F(\omega) = \int_{-\infty}^{+\infty} f(t)\, e^{-j\omega t}\, dt$$

The Fourier transform of the derivative of the function is

$$\mathcal{F}\left\{\frac{df(t)}{dt}\right\} = \int_{-\infty}^{+\infty} \frac{df(t)}{dt}\, e^{-j\omega t}\, dt$$

From integration by parts (see the Appendix) we have

$$\int_a^b u\,\mathrm{d}v = u[v]_a^b - \int_a^b v\,\mathrm{d}u$$

Thus, if we let $u = \mathrm{e}^{-\mathrm{j}\omega t}$ and $\mathrm{d}v = \mathrm{d}f(t)$, then

$$\mathcal{F}\left\{\frac{\mathrm{d}f(t)}{\mathrm{d}t}\right\} = \mathrm{e}^{-\mathrm{j}\omega t}[f(t)]_{-\infty}^{+\infty} - \int_{-\infty}^{+\infty} f(t)[-\mathrm{j}\omega\,\mathrm{e}^{-\mathrm{j}\omega t}]\,\mathrm{d}t$$

For the case where $\lim_{t\to-\infty} f(t) = \lim_{t\to\infty} f(t) = 0$ then

$$\mathcal{F}\left\{\frac{\mathrm{d}f(t)}{\mathrm{d}t}\right\} = \mathrm{j}\omega \int_{-\infty}^{+\infty} f(t)\,\mathrm{e}^{-\mathrm{j}\omega t}\,\mathrm{d}t$$

Thus

$$\mathcal{F}\left\{\frac{\mathrm{d}f(t)}{\mathrm{d}t}\right\} = \mathrm{j}\omega F(\omega)$$

For second derivatives we can repeat the above to obtain

$$\mathcal{F}\left\{\frac{\mathrm{d}^2 f(t)}{\mathrm{d}t^2}\right\} = (\mathrm{j}\omega)^2 F(\omega)$$

and, in general,

$$\mathcal{F}\left\{\frac{\mathrm{d}^n f(t)}{\mathrm{d}t^n}\right\} = (\mathrm{j}\omega)^n F(\omega) \qquad [28]$$

Example

Determine, by taking the derivative of the function, the Fourier transform of $f(t) = t\,\mathrm{e}^{-at}\,\mathrm{u}(t)$.

$$\frac{\mathrm{d}f(t)}{\mathrm{d}t} = \frac{\mathrm{d}}{\mathrm{d}t}t\,\mathrm{e}^{-at} = -at\,\mathrm{e}^{-at} + \mathrm{e}^{-at} = -af(t) + \mathrm{e}^{-at}$$

Taking the Fourier transform, since $\lim_{t\to-\infty} f(t) = \lim_{t\to\infty} f(t) = 0$, equation [26] gives

$$\mathrm{j}\omega F(\omega) = -aF(\omega) + \mathcal{F}\{\mathrm{e}^{-at}\}$$

where $F(\omega) = \mathcal{F}\{f(t)\}$. Using table 9.1, item 6, then

$$\mathrm{j}\omega F(\omega) = -aF(\omega) + \frac{1}{a + \mathrm{j}\omega}$$

Thus

$$F(\omega) = \frac{1}{(a + \mathrm{j}\omega)^2}$$

Review problems

9 Determine, by taking the derivative of the function, the Fourier transform of $f(t) = t^2 \mathrm{e}^{-at}$.

10 Determine the Fourier transforms of the first and second derivatives of the function $f(t) = \mathrm{e}^{-2t}$.

9.6 Transfer function

Fig. 9.17 The system

Suppose we have a system (figure 9.17) where, for example, there is an input which is a function of time $x(t)$ and a consequential output $y(t)$. The input and output are related by the differential equation

$$a_2 \frac{\mathrm{d}^2 y}{\mathrm{d}t} + a_1 \frac{\mathrm{d}y}{\mathrm{d}t} + a_0 y = bx$$

where a_2, a_1, a_0 and b are constants. If we take the Fourier transform of the differential equation, using equation [28], then we obtain

$$(\mathrm{j}\omega)^2 a_2 Y(\omega) + \mathrm{j}\omega a_1 Y(\omega) + a_0 Y(\omega) = bX(\omega)$$

where $Y(\omega)$ is the Fourier transform of $y(t)$ and $X(\omega)$ that of $x(t)$. Thus we can write

$$Y(\omega)[(\mathrm{j}\omega)^2 a_2 + \mathrm{j}\omega a_1 + a_0] = bX(\mathrm{w})$$

and hence

$$Y(\omega) = \left[\frac{b}{(\mathrm{j}\omega)^2 a_2 + \mathrm{j}\omega a_1 + a_0}\right] X(\omega)$$

or

$$Y(\omega) = H(\omega)X(\omega) \tag{29}$$

where, in this case,

$$H(\omega) = \left[\frac{b}{(\mathrm{j}\omega)^2 a_2 + \mathrm{j}\omega a_1 + a_0}\right]$$

$H(\omega)$ is called the *transfer function* of the system. It is the function which relates the Fourier transforms of the input and outputs.

Suppose that the input to the system is a unit-strength impulse. Then the Fourier transform of the input $X(\omega) = 1$. Thus, in this situation, $Y(\omega) = H(\omega)$. The output is

$$y(t) = \mathcal{F}^{-1}\{Y(\omega)\} = \mathcal{F}^{-1}\{H(\omega)\}$$

$y(t)$ is thus the impulse response of the system.

Example

A system has a transfer function of $2/(1 + j\omega)$. What will be its response to a unit-strength impulse input?

The input transform is that of a unit-strength impulse and so is 1. The output transform is thus

$$Y(\omega) = \frac{2}{1 + j\omega} \times 1$$

The output is $\mathcal{F}^{-1}$ $(Y(w)\}$. Item 6 in table 9.1 indicates that the function of time must be

$$y(t) = 2\ e^{-t}$$

Review problems

11 A system has a transfer function of $1/(5 + j\omega)$. Determine the response of the system to a unit-strength impulse.

12 A system has a transfer function of $1/(4 + j\omega)$. Determine the response of the system to a signum function

$$x(t) = +20 \text{ for } 0 \leq t < \infty$$
$$x(t) = -20 \text{ for } -\infty \leq t < 0$$

Hint: you will need to use partial fractions.

13 A system has a transfer function of $20/(8 + j\omega)$. Determine the response of the system to (a) a unit-strength impulse, (b) a unit-step input.

9.6.1 Electric circuits

For a resistor having only resistance R, then the current $i(t)$ is related to the potential difference across it, $v(t)$, by

$$v(t) = Ri(t)$$

Taking Fourier transforms gives

$$V(\omega) = RI(\omega)$$

Defining impedance $Z(\omega)$ as the ratio of the voltage transform to the current transform gives

$$Z(\omega) = \frac{V(\omega)}{I(\omega)} = R \qquad [30]$$

For an inductor having only inductance L, then $v(t) = L\ \mathrm{d}i(t)/\mathrm{d}t$ and so

$$V(\omega) = \mathrm{j}\omega LI(\omega)$$

Thus the impedance of the inductor is

$$Z(\omega) = \frac{V(\omega)}{I(\omega)} = \mathrm{j}\omega L \qquad [31]$$

For a capacitor having only capacitance C, then $i(t) = C\ \mathrm{d}v(t)/\mathrm{d}t$. Thus

$$I(\omega) = \mathrm{j}\omega CV(\omega)$$

and so the impedance is

$$Z(\omega) = \frac{V(\omega)}{I(\omega)} = \frac{1}{\mathrm{j}\omega C} \qquad [32]$$

The Fourier transforms can be said to give impedance values in the *frequency domain*. They give the same expressions for the impedances as are obtained using phasors and complex notation. The same techniques of circuit analysis can thus be used.

An alternative to considering the Fourier transform of each electrical component separately and then combining the transforms to give the overall transform of a circuit is to use Kirchhoff's laws. These can be used to determine the differential equation for the circuit as a whole and then determine the Fourier transform of this. The results are the same.

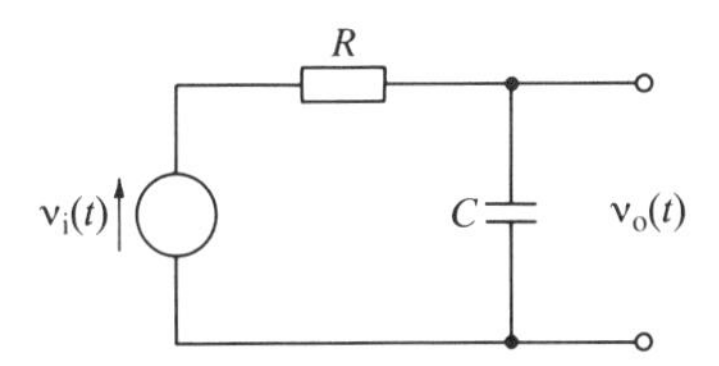

Fig. 9.18 Example

Example

Determine the transfer function for the electrical circuit shown in figure 9.18 and the circuit response when the input voltage is a unit-strength impulse.

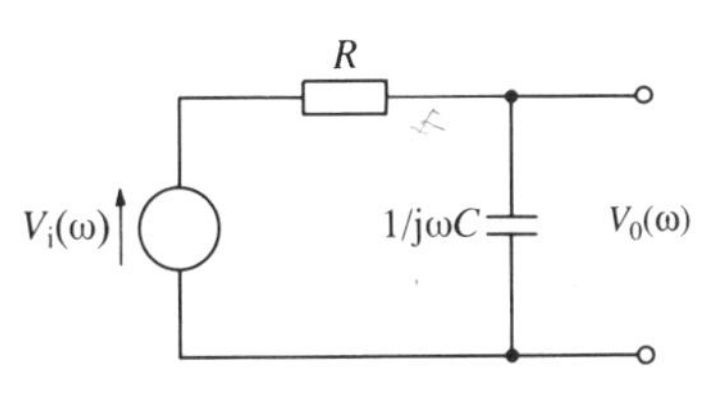

Fig. 9.19 Example

Figure 9.19 shows the circuit as it appears when in the frequency domain, i.e. when the Fourier transforms are used for impedances, voltages and currents. The voltage output across the capacitor can be obtained by voltage division. Thus

$$V_o(\omega) = \frac{1/j\omega C}{R + 1/j\omega C} V_i(\omega)$$

Thus the transfer function is

$$H(\omega) = \frac{V_o(\omega)}{V_i(\omega)} = \frac{1/j\omega C}{R + 1/j\omega C}$$

A unit strength impulse has a Fourier transform of $V_i(\omega) = 1$. Thus

$$V_o(\omega) = \frac{1/j\omega C}{R + 1/j\omega C} = \frac{1}{j\omega CR + 1} = \frac{1/CR}{(1/CR) + j\omega}$$

This is of the form given by item 6 in table 9.1. Thus

$$v_o(t) = \mathcal{F}^{-1}\{V_o(\omega)\} = (1/CR)\, e^{-t/CR}$$

Review problems

14 An electrical circuit consists of a resistance of 5 Ω in series with a capacitance of 1 F (this very large value has been chosen for simplicity). The output is the potential difference across the capacitor. Determine the transfer function for the system and the response when the input is a unit-strength impulse.

15 For the electrical circuit shown in figure 9.20, determine the transfer function and the response when the input is a unit-strength impulse.

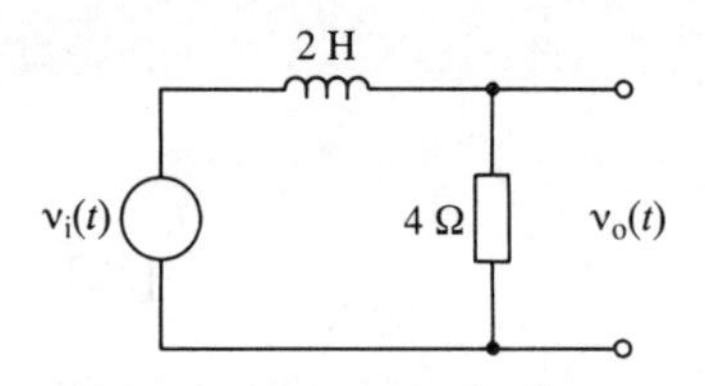

Fig. 9.20 Problem 15

9.7 Energy density

If $f(t)$ represents either the voltage across, or the current through, a resistance of 1 Ω, then the power developed will be $f^2(t)$. The total energy E over all time will thus be the integral of $f^2(t)$ over that time. Thus

$$E = \int_{-\infty}^{+\infty} f^2(t)\, dt$$

E is sometimes referred to as the 1-Ω energy. Considering $f^2(t)$ as $f(t) \times f(t) = f(t) \times \mathcal{F}^{-1}(\omega)$, where $\mathcal{F}^{-1}(\omega)$ is the inverse transform of $f(t)$ then we can write the above equation as

$$E = \int_{-\infty}^{+\infty} f(t)\, \mathcal{F}^{-1}(\omega)\, dt$$

Using equation [8] then

$$E = \int_{-\infty}^{+\infty} f(t)\left[\frac{1}{2\pi}\int_{-\infty}^{+\infty} F(\omega)\,\mathrm{e}^{\mathrm{j}\omega t}\,\mathrm{d}\omega\right]\mathrm{d}t$$

The result is a double integration. With such an equation we can interchange the order of the integration so that the inner integral is with respect to time and the outer one with respect to frequency. We can also rearrange terms to give

$$E = \frac{1}{2\pi}\int_{-\infty}^{+\infty} F(\omega)\left[\int_{-\infty}^{+\infty} f(t)\,\mathrm{e}^{\mathrm{j}\omega t}\,\mathrm{d}t\right]\mathrm{d}\omega$$

The inner integral would be the transform $F(\omega)$ of $f(t)$ if the exponential was $-\mathrm{j}\omega t$. However, if we consider negative times (see equation [22]) then the inner integral is $F(-\omega)$. We thus have

$$E = \frac{1}{2\pi}\int_{-\infty}^{+\infty} F(\omega)F(-\omega)\,\mathrm{d} \qquad [33]$$

Both $F(\omega)$ and $F(-\omega)$ are complex quantities. As indicated in section 9.2.1 we can write $F(\omega)$ in the form

$$F(\omega) = A(\omega) - \mathrm{j}B(\omega)$$

We can follow a similar reasoning to obtain

$$F(-\omega) = A(\omega) + \mathrm{j}B(\omega)$$

Thus $F(-\omega)$ is, what is termed, the complex conjugate of $F(\omega)$.

$$F(\omega) \times F(-\omega) = [A(\omega) - \mathrm{j}B(\omega)][A(\omega) + \mathrm{j}B(\omega)]$$

$$= A^2(\omega) + B^2(\omega)$$

However, $|F(\omega)| = \sqrt{A^2(\omega) + B^2(\omega)}$. Thus

$$F(\omega) \times F(-\omega) = |F(\omega)|^2 \qquad [34]$$

Thus equation [33] can be written in the time (the equation from which this analysis started) and frequency domains as

$$E = \int_{-\infty}^{+\infty} f^2(t)\,dt = \frac{1}{2\pi}\int_{-\infty}^{+\infty} |F(\omega)|^2\,\mathrm{d}\omega \qquad [35]$$

This relationship is known as *Parseval's theorem*. A similar relationship for the Fourier series was given in section 6.2.

Since $\omega = 2\pi f$ then equation [35] can be written as

$$E = \int_{-\infty}^{+\infty} |F(\omega)|^2 \, df$$

or, changing the limits,

$$E = 2\int_0^{+\infty} |F(\omega)|^2 \, df \qquad [36]$$

Equation [37] indicates that $|F(\omega)|^2$, when integrated with respect to frequency f, is proportional to the total energy in the signal. The area under a graph of $|F(\omega)|^2$, when plotted against f, is thus the total energy. Hence $|F(\omega)|^2$ can be considered to represent the *energy density*, i.e. the energy per unit bandwidth (J/Hz).

Example

A positive time exponential pulse $f(t) = 2\,e^{-3t}\,u(t)$ is applied to an ideal low-pass filter. What is the percentage of the total energy input which appears as output when the upper frequency cut-off is 2 Hz?

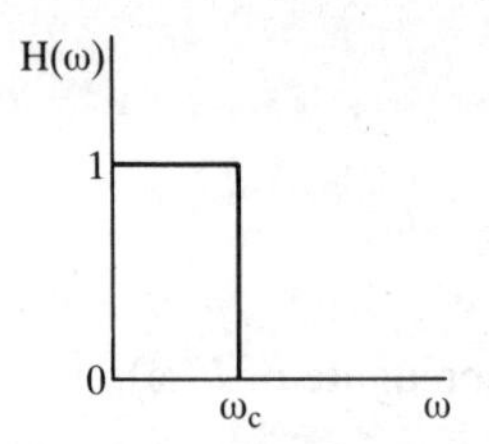

Fig. 9.21 Ideal low-pass filter

An *ideal filter* is one which allows all those frequency components of the output signal, within the pass band, to pass unattenuated from the input terminals to the output terminals. All frequencies outside this pass band are completely attenuated. Thus, for the ideal low-pass filter, the transfer function will be of the form shown in figure 9.21.

The Fourier transform of the input signal is given by item 6 in table 9.1 as $2/(3 + j\omega)$. Thus

$$|F(\omega|^2 = \frac{2}{3+j\omega} \times \frac{2}{3-j\omega} = \frac{4}{9+\omega^2}$$

The total energy in the input signal is given by equation [35] as

$$E = \frac{1}{2\pi}\int_{-\infty}^{+\infty} |F(\omega)|^2 \, d\omega = \frac{1}{2\pi}\int_{-\infty}^{+\infty} \frac{4}{9+\omega^2} \, d\omega$$

$$= \frac{4}{2\pi}\left[\frac{1}{3}\tan^{-1}\frac{\omega}{3}\right]_{-\infty}^{+\infty} = \frac{2}{3}\ \text{J}$$

The above is the energy obtained as a result of working in the frequency domain. We could, however, have obtained the total energy by working in the time domain. Thus

$$E = \int_{-\infty}^{+\infty} f^2(t)\, dt = \int_0^{+\infty} (2e^{-3t})^2 \, dt$$

$$= -\frac{4}{6}[e^{-6t}]_0^{+\infty} = \frac{2}{3}\ J$$

The pass band of the filter is between +2 Hz and 0 Hz, i.e. $+4\pi$ rad/s and 0 rad/s. The energy passed by the filter is thus given by equation [35] as

$$E = \frac{1}{2\pi}\int_0^{+4\pi} \frac{4}{9+\omega^2}\,d\omega = \frac{4}{2\pi}\left[\frac{1}{3}\tan^{-1}\frac{\omega}{3}\right]_0^{+4\pi}$$

$$= \frac{2}{3\pi}\left[\tan^{-1}\frac{4\pi}{3}\right] = 0.28\ J$$

Thus the percentage of the input which appears as output is (0.28/0.67) x 100 = 42%.

Example

An electrical circuit has a transfer function of $1/(1 + j\omega)$. What will be the percentage of the total 1-Ω energy at the input, which appears at the output in the frequency range 0 to 5 rad/s, when the input to the circuit is $e^{-t}u(t)$ V?

The total 1-Ω energy at the input is given by equation [35] as

$$E = \frac{1}{2\pi}\int_{-\infty}^{+\infty} |F(\omega)|^2\,d\omega$$

Since $f(t) = e^{-t}$ then item 6 in table 9.1 gives $F(\omega) = 1/(1 + j\omega)$. Hence

$$|F(\omega)|^2 = \frac{1}{1+j\omega} \times \frac{1}{1-j\omega} = \frac{1}{1+\omega^2}$$

Hence

$$E = \frac{1}{2\pi}\int_0^{+\infty} \frac{1}{1+\omega^2}\,d\omega = \frac{1}{2\pi}[\tan^{-1}\omega]_0^{+\infty} = \frac{1}{4}\ J$$

The output $Y(\omega)$ is given by

$$Y(\omega) = H(\omega)\,F(\omega)$$

where $H(\omega)$ is the transfer function. Thus

$$Y(\omega) = \frac{1}{1+j\omega} \times \frac{1}{1+j\omega}$$

$$|Y(\omega)|^2 = \frac{1}{(1+j\omega)^2} \times \frac{1}{(1-j\omega)^2} = \frac{1}{(1+\omega^2)^2}$$

Thus the energy appearing at the output is

$$E = \frac{1}{2\pi}\int_0^5 \frac{1}{(1+\omega^2)^2}\,d\omega$$

This integral can be solved by making the substitution $\omega = \tan\theta$. Then $d\omega = \sec^2\theta\,d\theta$ and so the integral becomes

$$\int \frac{1}{(1+\tan^2\theta)^2}\sec^2\theta\,d\theta = \int \frac{1}{(\sec^2\theta)^2}\sec^2\theta\,d\theta$$

$$= \int \cos^2\theta\,d\theta$$

$$= \int \tfrac{1}{2}(1+\cos 2\theta)\,d\theta$$

$$= \frac{\theta}{2} + \frac{1}{4}\sin 2\theta$$

Since $\sin 2\theta = 2\tan\theta/(1+\tan^2\theta)$ then we have for the energy

$$E = \frac{1}{2\pi}\left[\frac{1}{2}\tan^{-1}\omega + \frac{\omega}{2(1+\omega^2)}\right]_0^5 = 0.125\ \text{J}$$

Thus the percentage of the input energy which appears as output in this frequency range is $(0.125/0.25) \times 100 = 50\%$.

Review problems

16 The input to an ideal bandpass filter is 120 $e^{-24t}u(t)$ V. What percentage of the total 1-Ω energy at the input is passed by the filter? The pass band is between 24 rad/s and 48 rad/s.

17 The input to an ideal low pass filter is 2 $e^{-t/5}\,u(t)$. If the filter has a cut-off frequency of 0.2 rad/s, determine the percentage of the 1-Ω energy at the input which is passed by the filter.

18 If the voltage across a resistor with a resistance of 1 Ω is $t\,e^{-t/2}u(t)$ V, what will be the total energy absorbed by the resistor?

9.8 Convolution

Consider a system for which the input is $x(t)$ and the output $y(t)$. The input will be assumed to be some function which can be described in a general way by figure 9.22. We can approximately replicate this function by a series of rectangular pulses of uniform width $\Delta\lambda$. These pulses have the heights of $x(\lambda_0)$, $x(\lambda_1)$, ... $x(\lambda_i)$ at $t = \lambda_0, \lambda_1, \ldots \lambda_i$. Suppose we make $\Delta\lambda \to 0$, then each rectangular pulse will become an impulse. The strength of each impulse will be

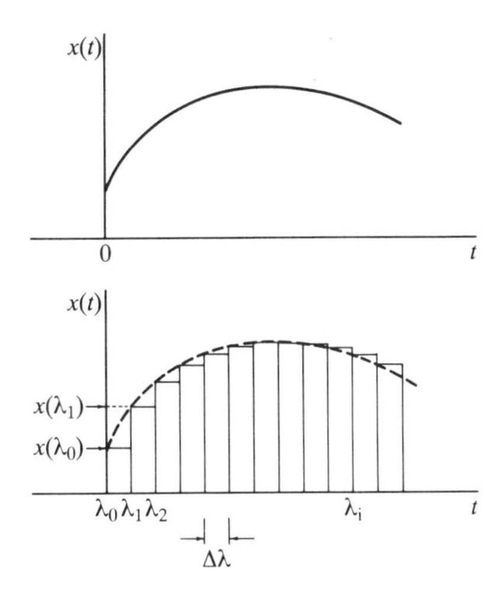

Fig. 9.22 Representing the input signal by rectangular pulses

the area enclosed by each of the rectangular pulses, i.e. $x(\lambda_0)\ \Delta\lambda$, $x(\lambda_1)\ \Delta\lambda$, ... $x(\lambda_i)\ \Delta\lambda$. Each impulse occurs at a different time. Thus we can represent the input function by

$$x(t) = x(\lambda_0)\ \Delta\lambda\ \delta(t-\lambda_0) + x(\lambda_1)\ \Delta\lambda\ \delta(t-\lambda_1) + x(\lambda_2)\ \Delta\lambda\ \delta(t-\lambda_2) + \ldots + x(\lambda_i)\ \Delta\lambda\ \delta(t-\lambda_i)$$

We can write this as

$$x(t) = \sum_{i=0}^{i=\infty} x(\lambda_i)\, \delta(t-\lambda_i)\, \Delta\lambda$$

As $\Delta\lambda \to 0$ then the summation approaches a continuous integral and we have

$$x(t) = \int_0^\infty x(\lambda)\, \delta(t-\lambda)\, \mathrm{d}\lambda$$

If $x(t)$ exists over all time then the lower limit of the integral becomes $-\infty$ and so, in general,

$$x(t) = \int_{-\infty}^{+\infty} x(\lambda)\, \delta(t-\lambda)\, \mathrm{d}\lambda \qquad [37]$$

The output from the system $y(t)$ will consist of the sum of the responses to each of these impulses. Suppose the output from the system for an impulse $\delta(t)$ is a function we can represent by $h(t)$, then the output from the system is

$$y(t) = \int_0^\infty x(\lambda)\, h(t-\lambda)\, \mathrm{d}\lambda \qquad [38]$$

The function $h(t)$ is often called the *unit-impulse function* or the *impulse response*. This integral is known as the *convolution integral*. In words it is stated as: *the output is equal to the input convolved with the impulse response*. It is often written as

$$y(t) = x(t) * h(t) \qquad [39]$$

where the asterisk is read as 'convolved with'.

Equation [38] sometimes appears in a different, but equivalent, form. If we let $z = t - \lambda$, then $\mathrm{d}\lambda = -\mathrm{d}z$ and so the equation becomes

$$y(t) = \int_{-\infty}^{+\infty} x(t-z)\, h(z)\, \mathrm{d}z \qquad [40]$$

Consider the Fourier transform of equation [38].

$$\mathcal{F}\,\{x(t) * h(t)\} = \mathcal{F}\left\{\int_{-\infty}^{+\infty} x(\lambda)\, h(t-\lambda)\, d\lambda\right\}$$

$$= \int_{-\infty}^{+\infty} \left[\int_{-\infty}^{+\infty} x(\lambda)\, h(t-\lambda)\, d\lambda \right] e^{-j\omega t}\, dt$$

$$= \int_{-\infty}^{+\infty} x(\lambda) d\lambda \int_{-\infty}^{+\infty} h(t-\lambda)\, e^{-j\omega t}\, dt$$

$$= \int_{-\infty}^{+\infty} x(\lambda) e^{-j\omega\lambda} d\lambda \int_{-\infty}^{+\infty} h(t-\lambda)\, e^{-j\omega(t-\lambda)}\, dt$$

The Fourier transform of the input $X(\omega)$ is the transform of equation [37] and, using the time shifting property, is given by the first of the above integrals. The second integral is the transform of the unit-impulse function and written as $H(\omega)$ and is known as the transfer function. The result is thus

$$\mathcal{F}\{y(t)\} = \mathcal{F}\{x(t) * h(t)\} = X(\omega)H(\omega) \qquad [41]$$

This is the equation [29] given earlier. Thus $\{x(t) * h(t)\}$ is the inverse transform of $X(\omega)H(\omega)$.

9.9 Relationship between the Fourier and Laplace transforms

The Fourier transform is given by

$$\mathcal{F}\{f(t)\} = F(\omega) = \int_{-\infty}^{+\infty} f(t)\, e^{-j\omega t}\, dt$$

while the Laplace transform is

$$\mathcal{L}\{f(t)\} = F(s) = \int_{0}^{+\infty} f(t)\, e^{-st}\, dt$$

where $s = \sigma + j\omega$. We can therefore rewrite this equation as

$$\mathcal{L}\{f(t)\} = F(s) = \int_{0}^{+\infty} f(t)\, e^{-\sigma t}\, e^{-j\omega t}\, dt$$

Thus, compared with the Fourier transform, the Laplace transform has an additional factor $e^{-\sigma t}$. For $\sigma > 0$ this means an exponentially decaying factor. This factor enables a wider variety of functions to be considered than with the Fourier transform. This is because we have problems in obtaining the Fourier transform for a function of time which does not approach zero as t approaches infinity, e.g. a function such as sin t. The presence of the exponentially decaying factor ensures that the integral with the Laplace transform will approach zero as t approaches infinity.

The Laplace transform also requires that functions should be zero for $t < 0$. The Fourier transform has, however, no such restrictions, being applicable to functions within $-\infty < t < +\infty$.

Further problems

19 Determine the Fourier transforms for the following signals:

(a) $f(t) = 0$ for $-2 > t$, $f(t) = 1 + t/2$ for $-2 < t < 0$,
$f(t) = 1 - t/2$ for $0 < t < 2$, $f(t) = 0$ for $2 < t$

(b) $f(t) = 0$ for $0 > t$, $f(t) = 1 - t$ for $0 \leq t < 1$

20 Use table 9.1 to obtain the Fourier transforms of the following functions: (a) 1, (b) $e^{-at}\,u(t)$, (c) $\sin \omega_0 t$.

21 Derive the Fourier transform for the function $\sin \omega_0 t$.

22 Derive, using the linearity principle, the Fourier transform for the function $e^{-t}u(t) + e^{-2t}u(t)$.

23 Determine the Fourier transform of a rectangular pulse which turns on at time 3, maintains its constant amplitude of 2, and then switches off at time 5.

24 Determine the Fourier transform of the function $\delta(t - 3)$, i.e. an impulse which is at a time of 3.

25 Determine, by taking the derivative of the function, the Fourier transform of the function described by figure 9.8.

26 Determine (a) the Fourier transform of e^{-at^2} and (b) the Fourier transform of the amplitude modulated cosine signal $e^{-at^2} \cos \omega_c t$.

27 If $\mathcal{F}\{f(t)\} = F(\omega)$ show that:

(a) $\mathcal{F}\left\{f\left(\frac{t}{a} + b\right)\right\} = |a|\, e^{jab\omega} F(a\omega)$,

(b) $\mathcal{F}\,\{e^{j\omega t} f(bt)\} = \frac{1}{|b|} F\left(\frac{\omega - a}{b}\right)$

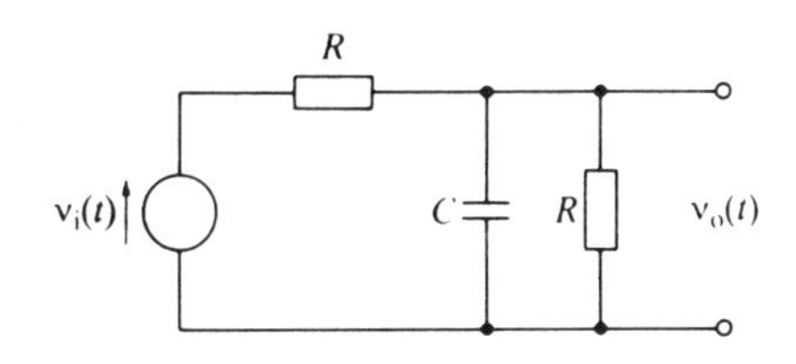

Fig. 9.23 Problem 28

28 Determine the transfer function of the circuit shown in figure 9.23 and the output when there is a unit strength impulse input.

29 If the circuit in figure 9.23 (problem 28) represents a filter circuit, what is the condition for the filter to give a distortion free output, i.e. the magnitude of the Fourier transform of the output is constant?

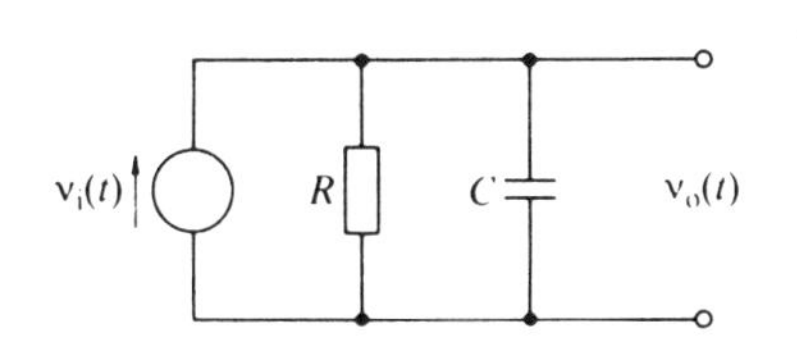

Fig. 9.24 Problem 30

30 Determine the transfer function of the circuit shown in figure 9.24 and the output when there is a unit strength impulse input.

31 A circuit consists of an inductance of 2 H in series with a resistance of 6 Ω. The output is the potential difference across the resistance. Determine the transfer function of the circuit and the response when there is an impulse input.

32 The input to an ideal low pass filter is $15\, e^{-5t}\, u(t)$. If the filter has a cut-off frequency of 10 rad/s, what will be the percentage of the 1-Ω energy at the input which is passed by the filter?

33 The input to an ideal bandpass filter is $6\, e^{-3t}u(t)$ V. If the filter

has a pass band between 1 Hz and 2 Hz, determine the percentage of the 1-Ω energy at the input which is passed by the filter.

34 A circuit consists of a capacitance of 10 μF in series with a resistance of 50 Ω. A step voltage of 5 V is applied to the circuit. What will be (a) the total energy and (b) the percentage of the total energy between 5 Hz and 500 Hz dissipated by the resistor?

35 A circuit consists of a resistance of 10 kΩ in series with a capacitance of 10 μF. The input to the circuit is a voltage of 15 e^{-5t} $u(t)$ V. The output is the voltage across the capacitor. Determine (a) the transfer function of the system, (b) the total energy available at the output, (c) the percentage of the output energy in the frequency bands 0 to 5 rad/s and 0 to 10 rad/s. Hint: partial fractions can be used to aid the integration of the integral.

36 The input signal to a circuit is $e^{-t}u(t)$ V. Derive an equation which relates the fraction of the energy of this signal appearing between 0 and a frequency ω.

Appendix
Supporting mathematics

The following is a brief review of some of the mathematics assumed in this book. For further details the reader is referred to the companion books in this series, in particular *Differentiation and integration* and *Complex numbers*.

Trigonometric functions

The following are the definitions of the six trigonometric functions. They are defined in terms of the sides of a right-angled triangle (figure Ap.1).

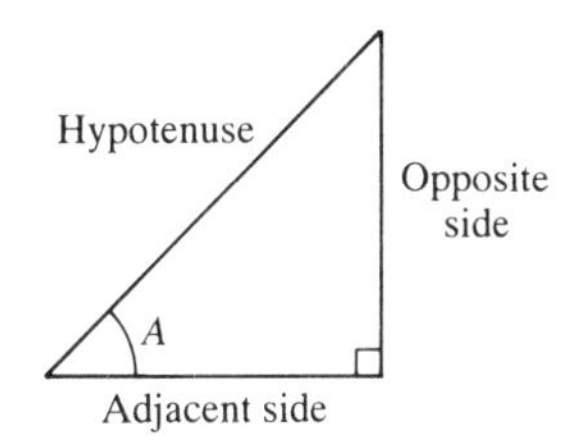

Fig. Ap.1 Right-angled triangle

$$\sin A = \frac{\text{side opposite angle}}{\text{hypotenuse}}$$

$$\cos A = \frac{\text{side adjacent to angle}}{\text{hypotenuse}}$$

$$\tan A = \frac{\text{side opposite angle}}{\text{side adjacent to angle}} = \frac{\sin A}{\cos A}$$

$$\text{cosec}\, A = \frac{1}{\sin A}$$

$$\sec A = \frac{1}{\cos A}$$

$$\cot A = \frac{1}{\tan A}$$

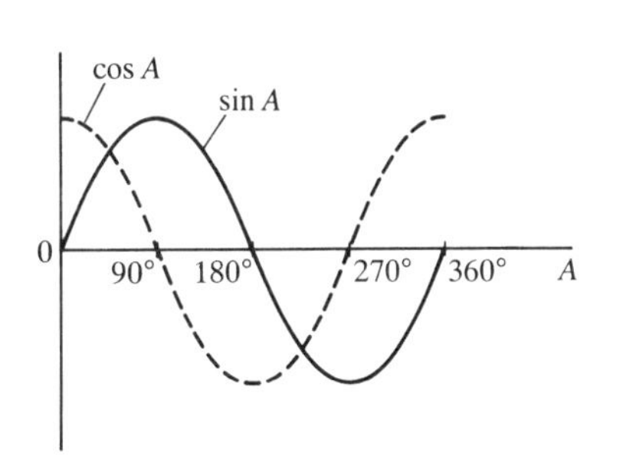

Fig. Ap.2 Sine and cosine functions

From the graphs of sin A and cos A against A in figure Ap.2, it is apparent that the value of cos A is the same as sin (A + 90°), i.e. we can consider that the cosine graph is just the sine graph displaced 90° to the left.

$$\cos A = \sin (A + 90°)$$

The value of sin A is always that of cos (A – 90°), i.e. we can consider that the sine graph is just that of the cosine graph displaced 90° to the right.

$$\sin A = \cos (A - 90^\circ)$$

Trigonometric relationships

The following is a summary of *trigonometric relationships*. Such relationships are often used in Fourier analysis to simplify equations:

$$\cos^2 A + \sin^2 A = 1$$

$$1 + \tan^2 A = \sec^2 A$$

$$\cot^2 A + 1 = \operatorname{cosec}^2 A$$

Compound angle addition and subtraction:

$$\sin (A + B) = \sin A \cos B + \cos A \sin B$$

$$\sin (A - B) = \sin A \cos B - \cos A \sin B$$

$$\cos (A + B) = \cos A \cos B - \sin A \sin B$$

$$\cos (A - B) = \cos A \cos B + \sin A \sin B$$

$$\tan (A + B) = \frac{\tan A + \tan B}{1 - \tan A \tan B}$$

$$\tan (A - B) = \frac{\tan A - \tan B}{1 + \tan A \tan B}$$

Double angle equations:

$$\sin 2A = 2 \sin A \cos A$$

$$\cos 2A = \cos^2 A - \sin^2 A = 2 \cos^2 A - 1 = 1 - 2 \sin^2 A$$

$$\tan 2A = \frac{2 \tan A}{1 - \tan^2 A}$$

Products into sums or difference equations:

$$\sin A \cos B = \tfrac{1}{2}[\sin (A + B) + \sin (A - B)]$$

$$\cos A \sin B = \tfrac{1}{2}[\sin (A + B) - \sin (A - B)]$$

$$\cos A \cos B = \tfrac{1}{2}[\cos(A+B) + \cos(A-B)]$$

$$\sin A \sin B = -\tfrac{1}{2}[\cos(A+B) - \cos(A-B)]$$

Sums or differences into products:

$$\sin A + \sin B = 2\sin\left(\frac{A+B}{2}\right)\cos\left(\frac{A-B}{2}\right)$$

$$\sin A - \sin B = 2\cos\left(\frac{A+B}{2}\right)\sin\left(\frac{A-B}{2}\right)$$

$$\cos A + \cos B = 2\cos\left(\frac{A+B}{2}\right)\cos\left(\frac{A-B}{2}\right)$$

$$\cos A - \cos B = -2\sin\left(\frac{A+B}{2}\right)\sin\left(\frac{A-B}{2}\right)$$

Inverse trigonometric functions

If $y = x^2$ then the *inverse function* is $x = \sqrt{y}$. The inverse function of $y = \sin x$ is written as $x = \sin^{-1} y$, or $x = \arcsin y$. Note that $\sin^{-1} y$ does *not* mean $1/\sin x$. Thus, suppose we have $y = \sin \pi/4$, then the inverse is $\pi/4 = \sin^{-1} y$. This can be read as $\pi/4$ radians is the angle whose sine is y.

Differentiation

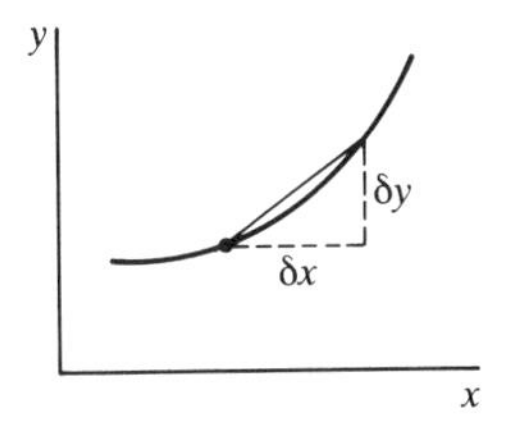

Fig. Ap.3 d*y*/d*x*

If we take two points on a graph of a function, as in figure Ap.3, then the value of $\delta y/\delta$, as we make x smaller, more closely approaches the value of the gradient of the tangent at a point on the graph. The gradient of the tangent is termed the *derivative* of a function, being denoted by $\mathrm{d}y/\mathrm{d}x$. Thus

$$\frac{\mathrm{d}y}{\mathrm{d}x} = \lim_{\delta x \to 0} \frac{\delta y}{\delta x}$$

The mathematical process of obtaining the derivative is called *differentiation*. The following are some general solutions of differentiation with respect to x, a being a constant:

$\frac{\mathrm{d}}{\mathrm{d}x}(a)$	0
$\frac{\mathrm{d}}{\mathrm{d}x}(ax^n)$	nax^{n-1}
$\frac{\mathrm{d}}{\mathrm{d}x}(\sin ax)$	$a\cos ax$

$\dfrac{\mathrm{d}}{\mathrm{d}x}(\cos ax)$	$-a\sin ax$
$\dfrac{\mathrm{d}}{\mathrm{d}x}(\mathrm{e}^{ax})$	$a\,\mathrm{e}^{ax}$
$\dfrac{\mathrm{d}}{\mathrm{d}x}(uv)$	$u\dfrac{\mathrm{d}v}{\mathrm{d}x}+v\dfrac{\mathrm{d}u}{\mathrm{d}x}$

u and v are both functions of x

Integration

If we have a function $y = x^2$ then we can differentiate it to obtain $\mathrm{d}y/\mathrm{d}x = 2x$. *Integration* is the mathematical process which reverses differentiation. Thus integrating $2x$ we obtain x^2. However, the derivative of $x^2 + 3$ is also $2x$. Thus in the integration of $2x$ we are not sure whether there is a constant term or not. Thus, a constant C is added to the result. Hence the integration of $2x$ is $2x + C$.

The following are some general solutions of integrations:

$\int ax^n\,\mathrm{d}x$	$\dfrac{ax^{n+1}}{n+1}+C$, except when $n=-1$
$\int \sin ax\,\mathrm{d}x$	$-\frac{1}{a}\cos ax+C$
$\int \cos ax\,\mathrm{d}x$	$\frac{1}{a}\sin ax+C$
$\int \sec^2 ax\,\mathrm{d}x$	$\frac{1}{a}\tan ax+C$
$\int \operatorname{cosec}^2 ax\,\mathrm{d}x$	$-\frac{1}{a}\cot ax+C$
$\int \mathrm{e}^{ax}\,\mathrm{d}x$	$\frac{1}{a}\mathrm{e}^{ax}+C$
$\int \frac{1}{x}\,\mathrm{d}x$	$\ln x+C$
$\int (u+v)\,\mathrm{d}x$	$\int u\,\mathrm{d}x+\int v\,\mathrm{d}x$

Integration by parts

This is a method of integrating a product of two terms and is widely used in this book. From the product rule of differentiation we have

$$\frac{\mathrm{d}}{\mathrm{d}x}(uv)=v\frac{\mathrm{d}u}{\mathrm{d}x}+u\frac{\mathrm{d}v}{\mathrm{d}x}$$

Rearranging this gives

$$u\frac{\mathrm{d}v}{\mathrm{d}x}=\frac{\mathrm{d}}{\mathrm{d}x}(uv)-v\frac{\mathrm{d}u}{\mathrm{d}x}$$

Integrating with respect to x gives

$$\int u \frac{dv}{dx} dx = \int \frac{d}{dx}(uv)\, dx - \int v \frac{du}{dx} d$$

and so

$$\int u\, dv = uv - \int v\, du$$

To illustrate the use of this equation, consider the integration

$$\int x \cos x\, dx$$

Let $u = x$. Then $du/dx = 1$ and so $du = dx$. Let $dv = \cos x\ dx$. Then $v = \int \cos x\, dx = \sin x$. Thus, substituting these values into the integration by parts equation gives

$$\int x \cos x\, dx = x \sin x - \int \sin x\, dx = x \sin x + \cos x + C$$

Integration as area under a curve

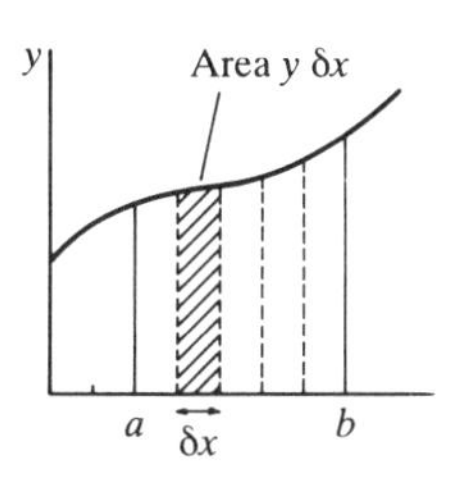

Fig. Ap.4 Area under a curve

The area under a graph of y against x between the values of x of a and b can be divided into a number of strips of width δx and height y (figure Ap.4). A single strip has thus an area $\delta A = y\ \delta x$. The total area is then the sum of all these strips between a and b. Thus

$$\text{area} = \text{sum of all strips between } x = a \text{ and } x = b$$

$$= \sum_{x=b}^{x=a} y\, \delta x$$

The accuracy of the area determined this way increases as the width of each strip is decreased. Thus, in the limit as δx tends to 0 we have

$$\text{area} = \lim_{\delta x \to 0} \sum_{x=b}^{x=a} y\, \delta x$$

We have for a strip $\delta A = y\ \delta x$. In the limit as δx tends to 0 then $\delta A/\delta x$ becomes $dA/dx = y$. Hence

$$\lim_{\delta x \to 0} \left(\frac{\delta A}{\delta x}\right) = \frac{dA}{dx} = y$$

$$dA = y\, dx$$

Integrating this with respect to x gives

$$\int_a^b dA = \int_a^b y\, dx$$

This is the total area under the curve between the limits a and b.

A consequence of this is that if we integrate a sine or cosine function over a period then, since the positive area and the negative area under the sine or cosine curves balance out, the value of the integral is zero.

Complex numbers

The roots of a quadratic equation $ax^2 + bx + c = 0$ are given by

$$x = \frac{-b \pm \sqrt{b^2 - 4ac}}{2a}$$

Thus with the equation $x^2 - 4x + 3 = 0$ we obtain $x = 2 \pm 1$. However, if $4ac$ is greater than b^2 we obtain the square root of a negative quantity. For example, with the equation $x^2 - 4x + 13 = 0$ we obtain $x = 2 \pm \sqrt{(-9)}$. There is no real number which has a negative square root. In order to cope with this problem we introduce a symbol j or i to represent $\sqrt{(-1)}$ Then we can write the solution as $x = 2 \pm \mathrm{j}3$. The j3 is said to be an *imaginary number*. We thus have roots made up of two parts, a real part and an imaginary part. Such a number is called a *complex number*. In general, a complex number z is represented by

$$z = a + \mathrm{j}b$$

where a is the real part and b the imaginary part. The roots in the example considered above are $x = 2 \pm \mathrm{j}3$, i.e. there are two roots of $x = 2 + \mathrm{j}3$ and $x = 2 - \mathrm{j}3$. Such a pair of numbers is called a *conjugate pair*, the complex conjugate being denoted by a star symbol. A complex conjugate pair are thus

$$z = a + \mathrm{j}b$$

$$z^* = a + \mathrm{j}b$$

If we plot the imaginary part of a complex number along the y-axis of a graph and the real part along the x-axis, then the result is called an *Argand diagram*. Figure Ap.5 shows such a diagram with a conjugate pair of points. Complex numbers that are in the form $a + \mathrm{j}b$ are said to be in *Cartesian form* since a and b give the Cartesian co-ordinates on a graph. However, we can specify a point on an Argand diagram by polar co-ordinates, i.e. specifying the length of a line joining the origin to the point and the angle the line makes with the axis. The length is called the modulus and represented by $|z|$ and the angle θ is termed the argument. Thus, in *polar form* we can specify a complex number by

Fig. Ap.5 Argand diagram

$$z = |z| \angle\theta$$

From figure Ap.5 it can be seen that we can convert complex numbers in Cartesian form to polar form by

$$|z| = \sqrt{(a^2 + b^2)}$$

$$\theta = \tan^{-1}\left(\frac{b}{a}\right)$$

and from polar form to Cartesian form by

$$a = |z| \cos \theta$$

$$b = |z| \sin \theta$$

These last two equations give

$$z = a + jb = |z| (\cos \theta + j \sin \theta)$$

Sines and cosines can be expressed as the following series, with the angle θ in radians,

$$\sin\theta = \theta - \frac{\theta^3}{3!} + \frac{\theta^5}{5!} + \ldots$$

$$\cos\theta = 1 - \frac{\theta^2}{2!} + \frac{\theta^4}{4!} + \ldots$$

Thus we can write z as

$$z = |z| \left(1 - \frac{\theta^2}{2!} + \frac{\theta^4}{4!} + \ldots\right) + j\,|z| \left(\theta - \frac{\theta^3}{3!} + \frac{\theta^5}{5!} + \ldots\right)$$

$$= |z| \left(1 + j\theta - \frac{\theta^2}{2!} - j\frac{\theta^3}{3!} + \frac{\theta^4}{4!} + \ldots\right)$$

Since $j^2 = -1$, $j^3 = -j$, $j^4 = 1$, etc. we can write the above equation as

$$z = |z| \left(1 + j\theta + j^2\frac{\theta^2}{2!} + j^3\frac{\theta^3}{3!} + j^4\frac{\theta^4}{4!} + \ldots\right)$$

However, this is just the series expansion of $e^{j\theta}$. Thus

$$z = |z|\, e^{j\theta}$$

This is termed the *exponential form* of a complex number.

Euler's formula

Since we have $z = |z|\ (\cos\theta + \mathrm{j}\sin\theta)$, the exponential form given above must mean that

$$e^{j\theta} = \cos\theta + j\sin\theta$$

This is known as *Euler's formula*.

With a negative value for θ we have, since $\cos(-\theta) = \cos\theta$ and $\sin(-\theta) = -\sin\theta$,

$$e^{-j\theta} = \cos\theta - j\sin\theta$$

Thus

$$e^{j\theta} + e^{-j\theta} = 2\cos\theta$$

and so

$$\cos\theta = \tfrac{1}{2}(e^{j\theta} + e^{-j\theta})$$

Since

$$e^{j\theta} - e^{-j\theta} = 2j\sin\theta$$

then

$$\sin\theta = \frac{1}{2j}(e^{j\theta} + e^{-j\theta})$$

Complex number algebra

With complex numbers in Cartesian form, then the sum of two complex numbers $(a + jb)$ and $(c + jd)$ is

$$(a + jb) + (c + jd) = (a + c) + j(b + d)$$

Their difference is

$$(a + jb) - (c + jd) = (a - c) + j(b - d)$$

Their product is

$$\begin{aligned}(a + jb)(c + jd) &= ac + j^2bd + j(ad + bc)\\ &= (ac - bd) + j(ad + bc)\end{aligned}$$

Their quotient is

$$\frac{a+\mathrm{j}b}{c+\mathrm{j}d} = \frac{a+\mathrm{j}b}{c+\mathrm{j}d} \times \frac{c-\mathrm{j}d}{c-\mathrm{j}d} = \frac{(ac+bd)+\mathrm{j}(bc-ad)}{c^2+d^2}$$

With complex numbers in polar form, then the product of two complex numbers $r_1\angle\theta_2$ and $r_2\angle\theta_2$ is

$$(r_1\angle\theta_2)(r_2\angle\theta_2) = (r_1 + r_2)\angle(\theta_1 + \theta_2)$$

and their quotient is

$$\frac{r_1\angle\theta_1}{r_2\angle\theta_2} = \frac{r_1}{r_2}\angle(\theta_1 - \theta_2)$$

Answers

Chapter 1

1 See figure A.1

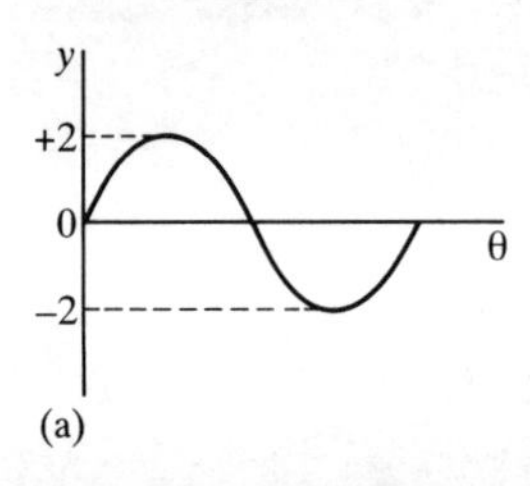

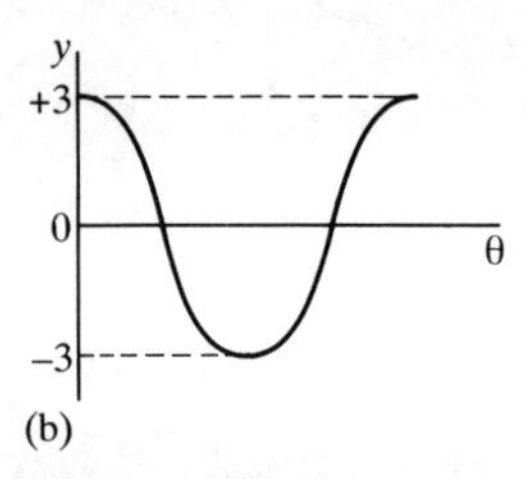

Fig. A.1 Chapter 1 Problem 1

2 (a) 3, (b) 1.5, (c) 0, (d) 1.5

3 (a) 1.68, (b) 1.82, (c) 0.28, (d) – 1.92

4 (a) 1.41, (b) 1.95, (c) 0.70

5 $y = 10 \sin 400t$, 400 rad/s = 63.7 Hz

6 500 Hz

7 $y = A/t$ for $0 \le t < T$

$y = A$ for $0 \le t < T/2$, $y = -A$ for $T/2 \le t < T$

8 See figure A.2

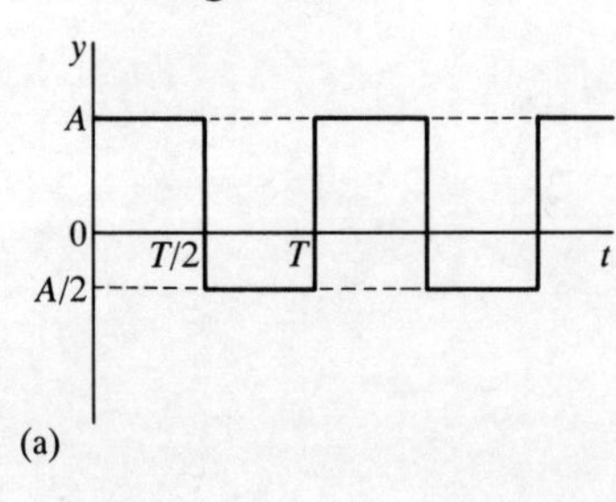

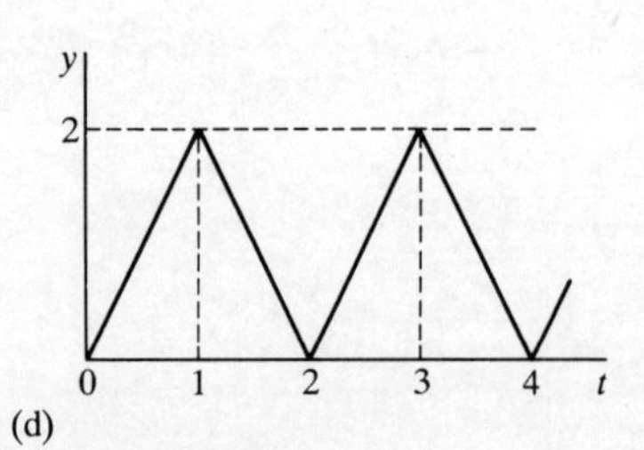

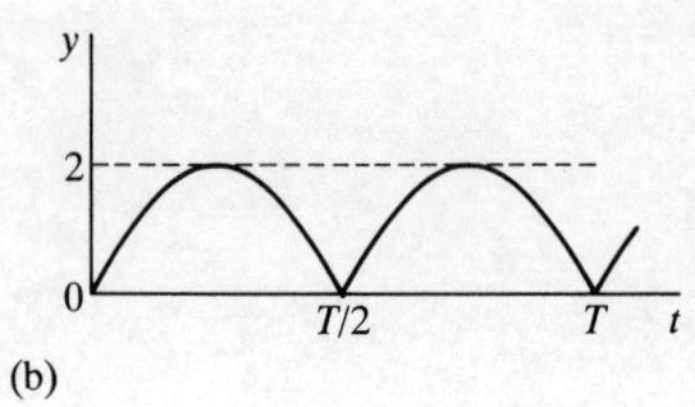

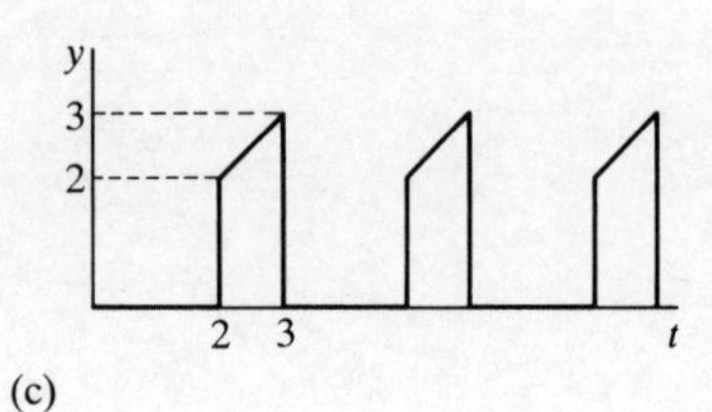

Fig. A.2 Chapter 1 Problem 8

9 (a) $y = 3$ for $0 \le t < 1$, $y = 0$ for $1 \le t < 3$, period 3,
(b) $y = 3 - 5t/3$ for $0 \le t < 3$, period 3,
(c) $y = 2$ for $0 \le t < 2$, $y = 6 - 2t$ for $2 \le t < 3$, period 3

10 See figure A.3

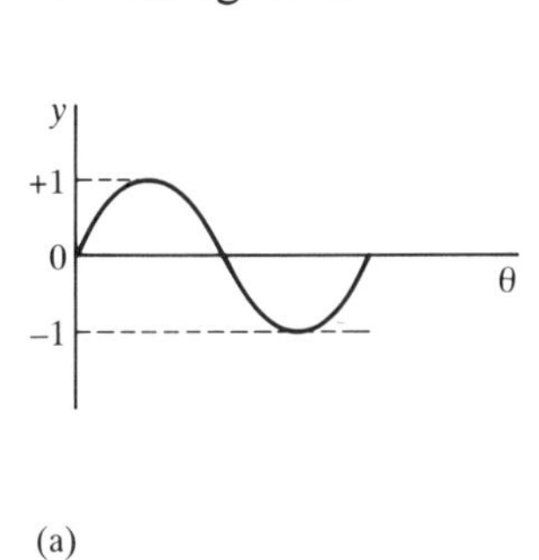

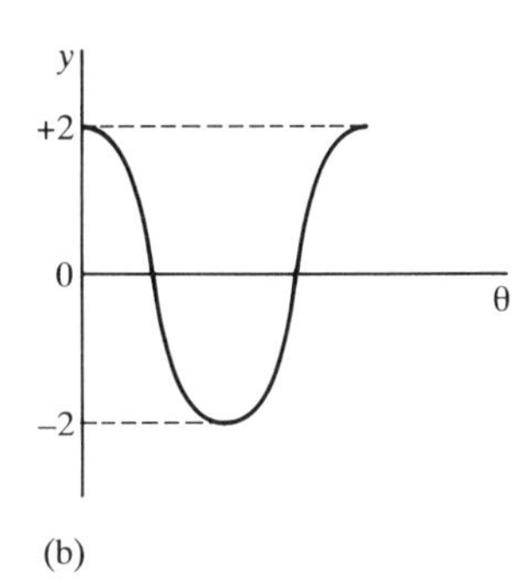

Fig. A.3 Chapter 1 Problem 10

11 (a) 0, (b) 3.46, (c) 4, (d) 3.46, (e) 0, (f) −3.46, (g) 3.46

12 (a) 4.21, (b) 4.55, (c) 0.71

13 (a) 8.66, (b) 10.0, (c) 8.89

14 40 Hz, 60 Hz

15 $y = 100 \sin 150t$, $y = 100 \sin 250t$

16 (a) $y = 2t/T$ for $0 \le t < T/2$, $y = 1$ for $T/2 \le t < T$,
(b) $y = 4$ for $0 \le t < 4$, $y = -2$ for $4 \le t < 6$,
(c) $y = 0$ for $0 \le t < 1$, $y = t/2 - 1/2$ for $1 \le t < 3$,
(d) $y = 2t$ for $0 \le t < 2$, $y = -2$ for $2 \le t < 4$

17 See figure A.4

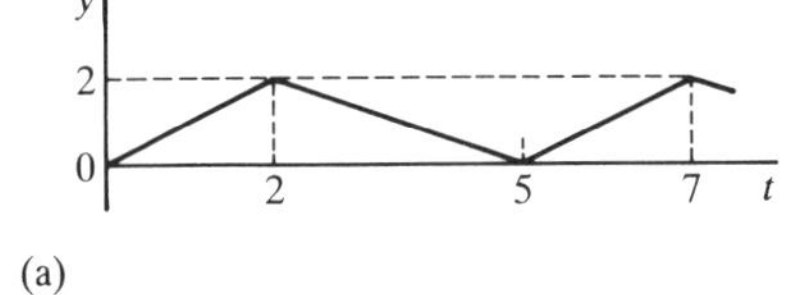

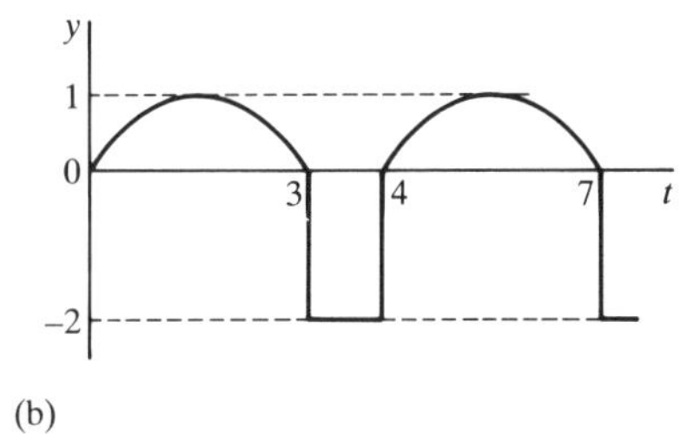

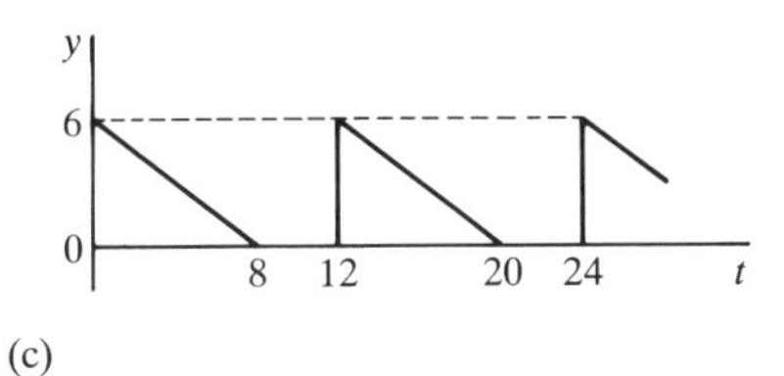

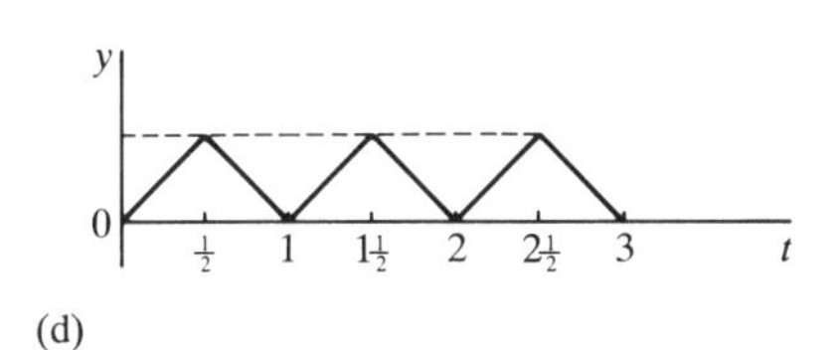

Fig. A.4 Chapter 1 Problem 17

Chapter 2

1 (a) Approximates to a half-wave rectified sine waveform,
(b) See figure A.5.

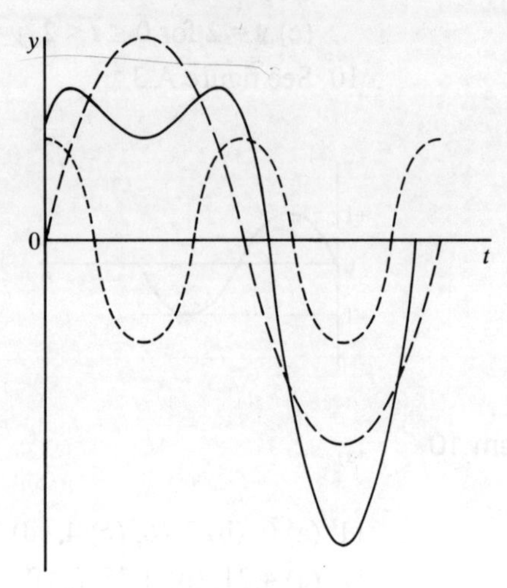

Fig. A.5 Chapter 2 Problem 1(b)

2 $y = -10 \cos (4t + 90°) = 10 \cos (4t - 90°)$

3 $y = 3.6 \cos (5t - 0.98)$ or $3.6 \sin (5t + 0.59)$

4 $y = 0.5 + 0.32 \cos (\omega t + 90°) + 0.16 \cos (\omega t + 90°)$
$+0.11 \cos (\omega t + 90°) + 0.08 \cos (\omega t + 90°)$
$+ 0.06 \cos (\omega t + 90°)$

5 See figure A.6

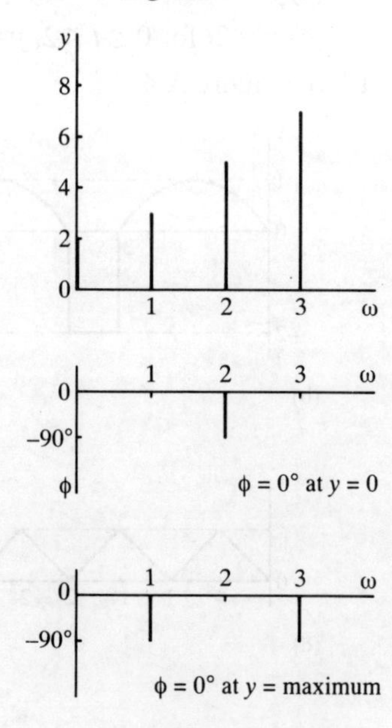

Fig. A.6 Chapter 2 Problem 5

6 $1.58 \cos (20t - 0.32)$

7 $5 \cos (t + 0.93)$

8 $\frac{4A}{\pi}\left(\sin \omega t + \frac{1}{3}\sin 3\omega t + \frac{1}{5}\sin 5\omega t + \ldots\right)$

9 $\frac{A}{2} - \frac{4A}{\pi^2}\left(\sin \omega t + \frac{1}{9}\sin 3\omega t + \frac{1}{25}\sin 5\omega t + \ldots\right)$

10 $\frac{A}{\pi} - \frac{4A}{3\pi}\cos \omega t - \frac{4A}{15\pi}\cos 2\omega t - \frac{4A}{35\pi}\cos 3\omega t - \ldots$

11 (a) $-\frac{8}{\pi^2}\left(\cos t + \frac{1}{9}\cos 3t + \frac{1}{25}\cos 5t + \ldots\right)$

(b) $1 - \frac{8}{\pi^2}\left(\cos t + \frac{1}{9}\cos 3t + \frac{1}{25}\cos 5t + \ldots\right)$

12 $\frac{\pi}{2} = 2\left(1 - \frac{1}{3} + \frac{1}{5} - \ldots\right)$

13 See figure A.7

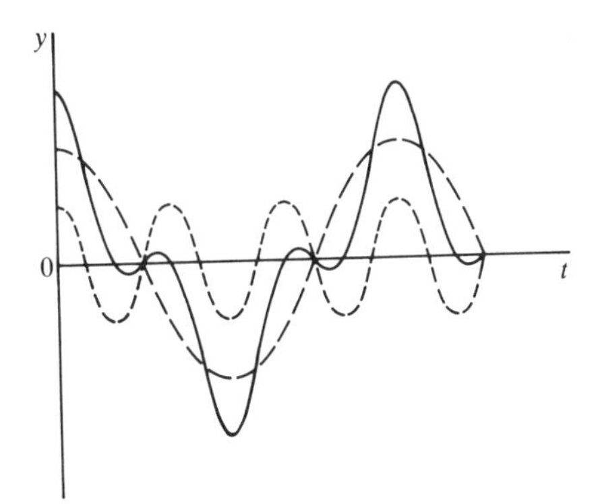

Fig. A.7 Chapter 2 Problem 13

14 3.6 cos $(5t + 0.98)$

15 3.6 cos $(10t - 0.98)$

16 (a) $\frac{A}{2} + \frac{2A}{\pi}\left(\cos t - \frac{1}{3}\cos 3t + \frac{1}{5}\cos 5t + \ldots\right)$

(b) $\frac{4A}{\pi^2}\left(\cos t + \frac{1}{9}\cos 3t + \frac{1}{25}\cos 5t + \ldots\right)$

(c) $\frac{4}{3}\pi^2 + 4\cos t + \cos 2t + \frac{4}{9}\cos 3t + \ldots - 4\pi \sin t - 2\pi \sin 2t$

$-\frac{4}{3}\pi \sin 3t - \ldots$

17 (a) $1 + \frac{4}{\pi}\sin\frac{\pi t}{5} + \frac{4}{3\pi}\sin\frac{3\pi t}{5} + \frac{4}{5\pi}\sin\frac{5\pi t}{5} + \ldots$

(b) $\frac{\pi}{4} - \frac{2}{\pi}\cos t - \frac{2}{9\pi}\cos 3t - \ldots - \sin t + \frac{1}{2}\sin 2t - \frac{1}{3}\sin 3t + \ldots$

(c) $\frac{2A}{\pi}\left(2\sin t + \frac{2}{3}\sin 3t + \frac{2}{5}\sin 5t + \ldots\right)$

(d) $\frac{\pi}{4} - \frac{2}{\pi}\cos t - \frac{2}{9\pi}\cos 3t - \frac{2}{25\pi}\cos 5t - \ldots + \sin t - \frac{1}{2}\sin 2t$

$+\frac{1}{3}\sin 3t - \frac{1}{4}\sin 4t + \ldots$

(e) $\frac{\pi}{4}-\frac{2}{\pi}\cos t-\frac{2}{9\pi}\cos 3t-\frac{2}{25\pi}\cos 5t-\ldots+\sin t-\frac{1}{2}\sin 2t$
$+\frac{1}{3}\sin 3t-\frac{1}{4}\sin 4t+\ldots$

(f) $\frac{1}{2}-\frac{10}{\pi}\left(\sin t+\frac{1}{3}\sin 3t+\frac{1}{5}\sin 5t+\ldots\right)$

(g) $\frac{\pi}{2}+\frac{4}{\pi}\left(\cos t+\frac{1}{9}\cos 3t+\frac{1}{25}\cos 5t+\ldots\right)$

(h) $\frac{\pi^2}{3}-4\left(\cos t-\frac{1}{4}\cos 2t+\frac{1}{9}\cos 3t+\ldots\right)$

18 $2\left(\sin x-\frac{1}{2}\sin 2x+\frac{1}{3}\sin 3x-\ldots\right)$, as given in problem

19 $\frac{4\pi^2}{3}+4\left(\cos x+\frac{1}{4}\cos 2x+\frac{1}{9}\cos 3x+\ldots\right)$
$-4\pi\left(\sin x+\frac{1}{2}\sin 2x+\frac{1}{3}\sin 3x+\ldots\right)$, as given in problem

Chapter 3

1 (a) Neither even or odd, (b) even, (c) odd, (d) even

2 (a) Even, (b) odd, (c) odd, (d) even

3 (a) Even, (b) odd, (c) even, (d) neither, (e) neither

4 (a) Even, (b) even, (c) even, (d) odd, (e) odd

5 (a) $2\left(\frac{\pi^2}{1}-6\right)\sin t-2\left(\frac{\pi^2}{2}-\frac{6}{8}\right)\sin 2t+2\left(\frac{\pi^3}{3}-\frac{6}{27}\right)\sin 3t-\ldots$,
(b) $\frac{\pi}{3}+2-4\cos t+1\cos 2t-\frac{4}{9}\cos 3t+\ldots$

6 (a) Sine, (b) cosine, (c) cosine, (d) sine, (e) cosine + sine, (f) sine

7 (a) 5, (b) 0, (c) 3

8 (a) $\pi+2\left(\sin t-\frac{1}{2}\sin 2t+\frac{1}{3}\sin 3t+\ldots\right)$
(b) $10+\frac{8}{\pi}\left(\sin t-\frac{1}{2}\sin 2t+\frac{1}{3}\sin 3t+\ldots\right)$
(c) $2+\frac{6}{\pi}\left(\sin t-\frac{1}{2}\sin 2t+\frac{1}{3}\sin 3t+\ldots\right)$

9 (a) $b_n = 1, 3, 5, \ldots$, (b) $a_n = 1, 3, 5, \ldots$, (c) $a_n = 0, 2, 4, \ldots$, (d) $b_n = 2, 4, 6, \ldots$

10 (a) Even, (b) even, (c) odd, (d) neither

11 (a) Even, (b) neither, (c) even, (d) even, (e) even, (f) odd, (g) even, (h) neither, (i) odd, (j) neither, (k) neither, (l) even, (m) even, (n) even, (o) odd, (p) even

12 (a) Sine, (b) sine, (c) cosine, (d) cosine + sine, (e) cosine, (f) cosine + sine

13 (a) $-2\left(\sin t+\frac{1}{2}\sin 2t+\frac{1}{3}\sin 3t+\ldots\right)$

(b) $\frac{\pi^2}{3}+\frac{4}{\pi}\left(-\cos t+\frac{1}{2}\cos 2t-\frac{1}{3}\cos 3t+\ldots\right)$

(c) $\frac{5}{\pi}\left(\sin t-\frac{1}{2}\sin 2t+\frac{1}{3}\sin 3t-\ldots\right)$

(d) $\frac{8}{\pi}\left(\sin t+\frac{1}{2}\sin 2t+\frac{1}{3}\sin 3t+\ldots\right)$

14 As given in the problem

15 As given in the problem

16 (a) $a_n = 0, 2, 4, \ldots$, (b) $a_n = 0, 2, 4, \ldots$, $b_n = 2, 4, 6, \ldots$,
(c) $b_n = 2, 4, 6, \ldots$, (d) $a_n = 1, 3, 5, \ldots$

17 (a) 5, (b) 0, (c) 2

Chapter 4

1 (a) 1, (b) $-\frac{8}{\pi^2}\left(\cos \pi t+\frac{1}{9}\cos 3\pi t+\frac{1}{25}\cos 5\pi t+\ldots\right)$

(c) $\frac{2}{\pi}-\frac{4}{\pi}\left(\frac{1}{3}\cos 2\pi t+\frac{1}{15}\cos 4\pi t+\frac{1}{35}\cos 6\pi t+\ldots\right)$

2 (a) $\frac{4}{\pi}\left(\sin \pi t+\frac{1}{3}\sin 3\pi t+\frac{1}{5}\sin 5\pi t+\ldots\right)$

(b) $\frac{2}{\pi}\left[\left(1-\frac{4}{\pi^2}\right)\sin \pi t-\frac{1}{2}\sin 2\pi t+\ldots\right]$

(c) $\frac{4}{\pi}\left(\sin\frac{\pi t}{2}+\frac{1}{2}\sin\frac{\pi t}{4}+\frac{1}{3}\sin\frac{\pi t}{6}+\ldots\right)$

3 (a) $2-\frac{16}{\pi^2}\left(\cos\frac{\pi t}{4}+\frac{1}{9}\cos\frac{3\pi t}{4}+\frac{1}{25}\cos\frac{5\pi t}{4}+\ldots\right)$,
$\frac{8}{\pi}\left(\sin\frac{\pi t}{4}-\frac{1}{2}\sin\frac{\pi t}{2}+\frac{1}{3}\sin\frac{3\pi t}{4}+\ldots\right)$

(b) $-\frac{8}{\pi}\left(-\frac{1}{3}\sin t+\frac{1}{15}\sin 3t+\frac{1}{105}\sin 5t+\ldots\right)$, $\frac{1}{2}-\frac{1}{2}\cos 2t$

(c) $\frac{1}{2}-\frac{2}{\pi}\left(\cos t-\frac{1}{3}\cos 3t+\frac{1}{5}\cos 5t-\ldots\right)$,
$\frac{2}{\pi}\left(\sin t-\sin 2t+\frac{1}{3}\sin 3t+\frac{1}{5}\sin 5t+\ldots\right)$

(d) $1-\frac{4}{\pi^2}\left(\cos \pi t+\frac{1}{9}\cos 3\pi t+\frac{1}{25}\cos 5\pi t+\ldots\right)$,
$\frac{2}{\pi}\left(\sin \pi t+\frac{1}{2}\sin 2\pi t+\frac{1}{3}\sin 3\pi t+\ldots\right)$

(e) $\frac{2}{3\pi}-\frac{12}{\pi}\left(-\frac{1}{5}\cos 2t+\frac{1}{7}\cos 4t+\frac{1}{27}\cos 6t+\ldots\right)$, $\sin 3t$

(f) $\cos t/2$, $\frac{8}{\pi}\left(\frac{1}{3}\sin t+\frac{2}{15}\sin 2t+\frac{3}{35}\sin 3t+\ldots\right)$

(g) $\frac{\pi}{2}+\frac{4}{\pi}\left(\cos t+\frac{1}{9}\cos 3t+\frac{1}{25}\cos 5t+\dots\right)$,

$2\left(\sin t+\frac{1}{2}\sin 2t+\frac{1}{3}\sin 3t+\dots\right)$

(h) $\frac{\pi}{4}+\cos t-\frac{1}{3}\cos 3t+\cos 5t-\dots$

$\sin t+\sin 2t+\frac{1}{3}\sin 3t+\frac{1}{5}\sin 5t+\dots$

4 $2\sin t+\sin 2t+\frac{2}{3}\sin 3t+\dots$

5 $\frac{\pi}{2}-\frac{4}{\pi}\left(\cos t+\frac{1}{9}\cos 3t+\dots\right)$

6 $y(x)=\frac{32y_0}{3\pi^2}\left(\sqrt{2}\sin\frac{\pi x}{L}+\frac{1}{4}\sin\frac{2\pi x}{L}+\frac{\sqrt{2}}{9}\sin\frac{3\pi x}{L}+\dots\right)$

7 As given in the problem

Chapter 5

1 $\frac{A}{2}-j\frac{A}{\pi}\left(e^{jt}+\frac{1}{3}e^{j3t}+\frac{1}{5}e^{j5t}+\dots\right)+j\frac{A}{\pi}\left(e^{-jt}+\frac{1}{3}e^{-j3t}+\frac{1}{5}e^{-j5t}+\dots\right)$

2 (a) $\frac{1}{2}-j\frac{1}{\pi}\left(e^{jt}+\frac{1}{3}e^{j3t}+\frac{1}{5}e^{j5t}+\dots\right)$

$+j\frac{1}{\pi}\left(e^{-jt}+\frac{1}{3}e^{-j3t}+\frac{1}{5}e^{-j5t}+\dots\right)$

(b) $0.637-0.212e^{j2\pi t}-0.424e^{j4\pi t}+\dots+0.212e^{-j2\pi t}+0.424e^{-j4\omega t}$

3 $4/\pi$, $4/3\pi$, $4/15\pi$, ..., all phases 0°

4 4.47, 63.4°

5 $3.2e^{j0.896}e^{j\omega t}+3.2e^{-j0.896}e^{-j\omega t}$

6 (a) $3e^{j4t}+3e^{-j4t}$, $3\angle 0°$ anticlockwise, $3\angle 0°$ clockwise,
(b) $3e^{j4t}e^{\pi/2}+3e^{-j4t}e^{-\pi/2}$, $3\angle(\pi/2)$ anticlockwise, $3\angle(-\pi/2)$ clockwise

7 $3.2e^{j2\omega t}e^{j0.90}+3.2e^{-j2\omega t}e^{-j0.90}$, $3.2\angle 0.90$ rotating anticlockwise, $3.2\angle(-0.90)$ rotating clockwise

8 (a) $1+j\frac{1}{4}\left(e^{j\pi/4}+\frac{1}{2}e^{j2\pi/4}+\frac{1}{3}e^{j3\pi/4}+\dots\right)$

$+j\frac{1}{4}\left(e^{-j\pi/4}+\frac{1}{2}e^{-j2\pi/4}+\frac{1}{3}e^{-j3\pi/4}+\dots\right)$

(b) $-\frac{1}{2}-j\frac{3}{\pi}\left(e^{j\pi t/3}+\frac{1}{2}e^{j2\pi t/3}+\frac{1}{3}e^{j3\pi t/3}+\dots\right)$

$-j\frac{3}{\pi}\left(e^{-j\pi t/3}+\frac{1}{2}e^{-j2\pi t/3}+\frac{1}{3}e^{-j3\pi t/3}+\dots\right)$

(c) $0.667+0.456e^{j2\pi t/3}+0.114e^{j4\pi t/3}+\dots+0.456e^{-j2\pi t/3}$
$+0.114e^{-j4\pi t/3}+\dots$

9 1, $6/\pi$, $3/\pi$, $2/\pi$, ...; 0° for $n = 0$ and 90° for the rest

10 8, $32/\pi$, $16/\pi$, $32/3\pi$, ...; 0° for $n = 0$ and −90° for the rest

11 $10 + 5e^{-j0.644}\,e^{j\omega t} + 3.2e^{j0.896}e^{j2\omega t} + \ldots + 5e^{j0.644}e^{-j\omega t} + 3.2e^{-j0.896}e^{-j2\omega t} + \ldots$

12 $0.5 + 0.203e^{-j\pi t} + 0.023e^{-j3\pi t} + 0.008e^{-j5\pi t} + \ldots + 0.203e^{j\pi t} + 0.0203e^{j3\pi t} + 0.008e^{j5\pi t} + \ldots$

13 $1e^{j2t}e^{\pi/6} + 1e^{-j2t}e^{-\pi/6}$, $1\angle(-\pi/3)$ anticlockwise, $1\angle(\pi/3)$ clockwise

14 See figure A.8.

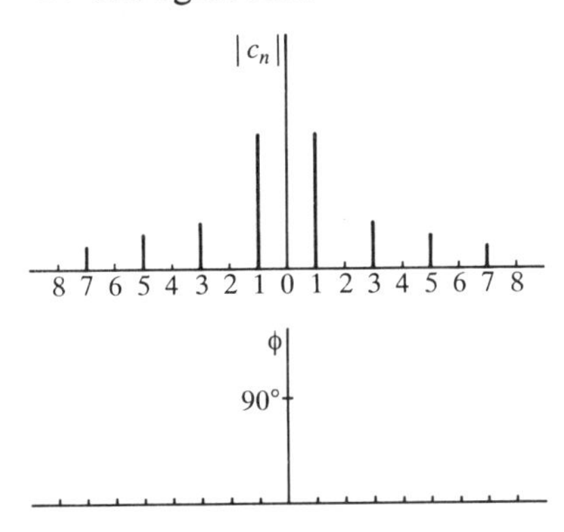

Fig. A.8 Chapter 5 Problem 14

Chapter 6

1 $v = 40 \sin 500t + 20 \sin 1000t$ V

2 $i = 3.2 \cos(100t + 90°) + 3.2 \cos(200t + 90°)$ mA

3 500 Ω, 250 Ω, 125 Ω

4 $i = 35.36 \sin(1000t + 45°) + 18.95 \sin(2000t - 63.4°)$ A

5 63.7 V, 21.2 V, 2.1 V

6 $v_{out} = \dfrac{4V_m}{\pi} \sum_{n=1}^{n=\infty} \dfrac{\sin(n\omega t - \alpha)}{n\sqrt{1 + (n\omega RC)^2}}$ with $\alpha = \tan^{-1} n\omega RC$

7 $58 \sin(1000t - 31°) + 8.0 \sin 2000t + 6.3 \sin(3000t + 72°)$ mA

8 $20 \sin(500t + 9.5°) + 17 \sin(1500t + 49.6°)$ mA

9 77.5 V

10 14.4 mA

11 53.1 W, 0.85

12 3.29 W, 0.14

13 $i = 0.5 + 0.32 \sin 500t + 0.16 \sin 1000t + 0.11 \sin 1500t$ mA

14 200 Ω, 100 Ω, 50 Ω

15 $\frac{V_m}{2R} + \frac{2V_m}{\pi} \sum_{n=1}^{n=\infty} \frac{\sin(n\omega t - \alpha)}{n\sqrt{R^2 + (n\omega L)^2}}$ with $\alpha = \tan^{-1} n\omega L/2$

16 12.7 sin $(500t + 72°)$ + 4.1 sin $(1500t - 59°)$ mA

17 250 + 395 cos $(62.6t - 71.9°)$
+ 18.3 cos $(188.5t - 74.2°)$ + ... μA

18 0.36 A

19 0.97 V

20 9.33 mA

21 51 W

22 168 W, 0.82

23 87.6 mW

24 101 W

25 15.7 W, 0.43

26 4.90 W, 0.30

27 As problem

Chapter 7

1 10 square units

2 1 square unit

3 $i = 50 \cos 2t + 17 \cos 3t + 150 \sin t + 87 \sin 2t + 47 \sin 3t$

4 $y = 26.5 + 10.2 \cos t - 9.1 \cos 2t + 27 \cos 3t + 13.1 \sin t$
$+ 2.0 \sin 2t + 0.3 \sin 3t$

5 $y = 1.2 + 10 \sin t + 4.2 \sin 3t$

6 $y = 20 + 10 \cos t + 5 \cos 2t + 1 \cos 3t$

7 $y = 10 \cos t + 1 \cos 3t + 10 \sin t + 4 \sin 3t$

8 See table 2.1, item 2

9 $y = 41.3 - 8.5 \cos t - 5.5 \cos 2t - 16.9 \cos 3t + 14.3 \sin t$
$+ 5.3 \sin 2t - 0.4 \sin 3t$

10 $i = 114 \cos t - 102 \cos 3t + 606 \sin t + 640 \sin 3t$

11 $y = 1.4 - 6.6 \cos t + 51 \cos 2t + 3 \cos 3t + 126 \sin t$
$+ 31 \sin 2t + 9 \sin 3t$

12 $y = 54 - 54 \cos 2t - 4 \cos 4t$

Chapter 8

1 $\frac{2}{\pi}\left(\frac{1}{3}\sin t + \frac{2}{15}\sin 2t + \ldots\right)$, valid

2 $\frac{16}{\pi}\left(\sin t - \frac{1}{3}\sin 3t + \frac{1}{5}\sin 5t - \ldots\right)$, valid

3 $2\left(-\cos t+\frac{1}{4}\cos 2t-\frac{1}{9}\cos 3t+\ldots\right)$

4 (a) $y = A\cos 2t + B\sin 2t + \frac{1}{3}\sin t$

(b) $y = A\cos 2t + B\sin 2t + 0.33\sin t - 0.02\sin 3t$
$- 0.002\sin 5t$

5 (a) $y = A\cos 0.71t + B\sin 0.71t - 1.33\sin t$

(b) $y = A\cos 0.71t + B\sin 0.71t - 1.33\sin t - 0.013\sin 3t$

(c) $y = A\cos 0.71t + B\sin 0.71t + 1.64 + 2\cos t$
$+ 0.071\cos 2t + \ldots$

6 $y = A\cos 3t + B\sin 3t + \frac{1}{\pi}\left(\frac{1}{3}\sin t+\infty\sin 3t+\frac{1}{750}\sin 5t+\ldots\right)$

7 $5.0\sin t + 3.6\sin 2t + 0.6\sin 3t$, valid

8 (a) $y = A\cos 4t + b\sin 4t + 0.067\sin t$

(b) $y = A\cos 4t + B\sin 4t + 0.07\sin t + 0.02\sin 3t$
$- 0.0004\sin 5t$

9 (a) $y = A\cos 1.41t + B\sin 1.41t + \sin t$

(b) $y = A\cos 1.41t + B\sin 1.41t + 0.33\sin t - 0.02\sin 3t$
$- 0.0002\sin 5t$

10 $y = C\cos\sqrt{\frac{k}{m}}\,t + D\sin\sqrt{\frac{k}{m}}\,t + \frac{A}{\sqrt{(k/m)-\omega^2}}\cos\omega t$

11 $y = A\cos\sqrt{10}\,t + B\sin\sqrt{10}\,t$
$+\frac{80}{\pi}\left[\frac{1}{40-\pi^2}\sin\frac{\pi t}{2}-\frac{1}{40-4\pi^2}\sin\frac{2\pi t}{2}-\ldots\right]$

Chapter 9

1 (a) 1, 0, (b) $2/\omega$, $\pi/2$, (c) $1/\sqrt{2+\omega^2}$, $\tan^{-1}\omega/2$

2 (a) $\frac{2(1-\cos\omega)}{j\omega}$, (b) $\frac{2a}{a^2+\omega^2}$

3 $2/j\omega$

4 (a) $\pi\delta(\omega) + 1/j\omega$, (b) $2\pi\delta(\omega)$, (c) $\pi[\delta(\omega+\omega_0)+\delta(\omega-\omega_0)]$

5 $\pi\delta(\omega) + 1/j\omega$

6 (a) Imaginary, (b) imaginary, (c) real, (d) real

7 $\frac{e^{-j4\omega}}{1+j\omega}$

8 $2\frac{\sin(\omega-3)}{(\omega-3)}$

9 $\frac{2}{(a+j\omega)^3}$

10 $j\omega\left(\frac{1}{a+j\omega}\right)$, $(j\omega)^2\left(\frac{1}{a+j\omega}\right)$

11 $y(t) = e^{-5t}$

12 $5 \text{ sqn } t - 10\, e^{-4t}u(t)$, $5 \text{ sqn } t$ is a signum function −5 to +5

13 (a) $20\, e^{-8t}u(t)$, (b) $(2.5 - 2.5\, e^{-8t})u(t)$

14 $\frac{1/5}{(1/5)+j\omega}$, $\frac{1}{5}e^{-t/5}$

15 $\frac{2}{2+j\omega}$, $2\, e^{-2t}$

16 20.5%

17 50%

18 2 J

19 (a) $\frac{1-\cos 2\omega}{\omega^2}$, (b) $\frac{1}{j\omega}+\frac{1}{\omega^2}(1-e^{-j\omega})$

20 (a) $2\pi\delta(\omega)$, (b) $1/(a+j\omega)$, (c) $j\pi[\delta(\omega+\omega_0)-\delta(\omega-\omega_0)]$

21 $j\pi[\delta(\omega+\omega_0)-\delta(\omega-\omega_0)]$

22 $\frac{1}{1+j\omega}+\frac{1}{2+j\omega}$

23 $e^{-j4\omega}\frac{4\sin\omega}{\omega}$

24 $e^{-j\omega 3}$

25 $\frac{2(1-\cos\omega)}{j\omega}$

26 (a) $\sqrt{\frac{\pi}{a}}\, e^{-\omega^2/4a}$, (b) $\frac{1}{2}\sqrt{\frac{\pi}{a}}\, e^{-(\omega-\omega_c)^2/4a}+\frac{1}{2}\sqrt{\frac{\pi}{a}}\, e^{-(\omega+\omega_c)^2/4a}$

27 As given in problem

28 $\frac{1}{2+jRC\omega}$, $\frac{1}{RC}e^{-2t/RC}u(t)$

29 $\left(\frac{2}{RC}\right) >> \omega$

30 $\frac{R}{1+j\omega CR}$, $\frac{1}{C}e^{-t/RC}u(t)$

31 $\frac{3}{3+j\omega}$, $3\, e^{-3t}u(t)$

32 66.7%

33 13.4%

34 (a) 125 μJ, (b) 62.9%

35 (a) $10/(10+j\omega)$, (b) 15 J, (c) 7.7%, 91.0%

36 $\frac{2}{\pi}\tan^{-1}\omega$

Index